130-1 Lock, steel $200-250
Lock, brass $250-300
2 Bulldog head $100-125

131-1 Haversacks $150-200

132-1 Wooden sign $750-1000

133-1 Call cards
a American Express $175-225
b Wells Fargo-left FAKE
c Wells Fargo-right $250-400
d Adams $175-225

134-1 Adams porcelain $250-300
2 Wells Fargo porcelain $350-500
3 American porcelain $85-125

135-1 American Railway $75-100
2 Railway Express $45-65
3 Railway Express $35-50
4 Lithograph $175-200
5 Western Union $75-125
6 Wells Fargo Express $375-500

136-1 Catalog $65-85
Coin, holder and envelope $85-125
2 Hats and Badges
a Aluminum $150-200
b Nickeled brass $200-250
c Celluloid $100-150
d Lithographed $125-175

137-1 Cased coin and letter $175-250
FAKE coin
2 Express envelope $20-35

138-1 Package scales $250-375
2 Air Express $75-125
3 Package scale $225-350

139-1 American Express $350-400
American Railway Express $150-200
Railway Express Agency $45-65

## ADVERTISING

140-1 Winchester $275-350

141-1 Remington $275-350
2 Winchester $275-350

142-1 Remington Arms $175-225
2 Winchester $450-550
3 Austin Powder Co. $400-500
4 Winchester $275-350
5 Harrington & Richardson $275-350

143-1 Infallible Powder $350-450

144-1 Peters $175-225
2 Peters $225-275
3 Winchester $275-350
4 Union Metallic $225-275
5 Peters $225-275
6 Winchester $275-350

145-1 Hopkins Allen $275-350
2 Winchester $275-350

146-1 Ithaca Guns $325-375
2 Union Metallic $225-275

## WESTERN PHOTOGRAPHY

149-1 Texas Rangers $350-400

150-1 Brown, Henry $1500-2000

151-1 Hunter $125-175

152-1 Cowboy $65-85

153-1 Buckskinner $65-85

154-1 Bank $100-125
2 Cowboy $75-100
3 Store $100-125

155-1 Virgil Earp - Rare

156-1 peasant $100-125
2 Cowboys $65-85
3 ''Big Foot'' $175-250

157-1 Texas Rangers $100-150
2 Dalton Gang $275-350

158-1 Cody $125-175
2 Carson $125-175

159-1 Custer $135-165

160-1 Indian $50-75
2 prisoner $125-175
3 stereo $35-65

## RUSTY RELICS

162-1 Top: $145-165
Center: $135-150
Bottom: $100-125

163-1 $175-200

164-1 Top: $115-135
Center: $95-110
Bottom: $75-95
flask: $35-50

165-1 Top: $135-165
Bottom: $75-95

166-1 Top: $135-165
Center: $100-125
Bottom: $85-100
2 Top: $135-165
Center: $95-110
Bottom: $20-35

167-1 Top: $450-650
Center: $65-75
Bottom: $85-100

168-1 Top: $45-65
Bottom: $40-55
2 $250-350
3 Top: $85-95
Center: $45-65
Bottom: $135-165

169-1 $200-250

170-1 Top: $65-85
Left: $75-85
Right: $50-65

Bottom: $35-40
2 Top: $65-75
Bottom: $45-65

171-1 Top: $65-85
Center: $85-100
Bottom: $65-85

## THE BADGE

174-1 Gun and Badge - Rare

175-1 hat band $175-225

176-1 Marshal $85-125
2 Dallas $225-275
3 Galveston $275-350
4 Butte $175-225
5 Police $175-225
6 gold - Rare
7 Lander $150-175
8 Chief $350-450
9 Police $35-65

179-1 Deputy Marshal - Rare
2 Custer Co. $175-225
3 Police $135-165

180-1 ribbon $165-185
2 Denver $450-550
3 Sergeant $300-400
4 Sheriff $175-200
5 Marshal $250-350
6 Chief $300-400
7 Marshal $150-200

181-1 Top: club $35-65
Left: Come-along $65-85
Right: Come-along $35-50

182-1 whistles $10-25
double whistles $35-65
ivory whistles $85-125
matchsafe $85-125
watch $275-350

183-1 Top: with flask $250-300
Center: with tassels $85-125
Bottom: with ivory and gold $750-1000

184-1 Judge - Rare
2 Snohomish $100-125
3 stock $65-85
4 Marshal $375-450
5 Constable $125-175
6 Nevada $135-165
7 Los Angeles $175-225
8 Sheriff $85-125
9 Nevada $125-175

186-1 Top: $85-125
Center: $65-85
Bottom: $85-110

187-1 Left: $85-125
Center: $125-150
Right: $65-85

188-1 Top left: $175-225
Top right: $65-85
Center: $85-125
Bottom left: $225-275
Bottom right: $125-175

## COWBOYS CHAPS

78-1 Shotguns $350-425
   2 Rough-out britches $125-150

79-1 Leather britches $150-175
   2 Working batwings $175-225
   3 Black woolies $350-400

## COWBOY CUFFS

80-1 $65-85
   2 $50-75

81-1 $125-175
   2 $100-150
   3 $85-110
   4 $100-125

## THE WESTERN SALOON

86-1 Maryland $45-65
   Keystone $55-75
   Little Straight $85-110
   Douglas $150-175
   2 Old Kirk $250-300
   Claret $250-300
   Elk's Pride $250-300
   Kellerstone $325-375

87-1 Kentucky Tavern $45-65
   Diamond Crown $65-85
   Hotaling $50-65
   2 Pinch bottles $175-275

88-1 United We Stand $65-85
   Old Metropolitan $45-55
   Rum $100-125
   Tucker Special $125-150
   2 Famous Atherton $110-135
   Monogram and Livingston $60-85
   Cyrus Noble $65-85
   3 Old Grand-Dad $250-300
   Rose-Bud $350-400
   Custer's Reserve $500-650
   Old Hickory $250-300

89-1 Wine, Port, Bitters $350-450
   Sanfter Heinrich $400-500

90-1 Pocket Flasks $125-250
   2 Pretzel bowl $250-300
   Mug $85-125
   Bouquet Whiskey $350-400

91-1 Jockey Club - Rare
   Thimble jigger $35-50
   etched jigger $10-25
   Consumer's mug - Rare

92-1 Ivory chips $10-25
   Derringer $375-550
   Poker "Buck" - Rare
   mirrors $65-125
   Cigar cutters $65-125
   Matchsafes $65-125
   2 Gold watch and chain - Rare
   Cigar case $175-250
   Derringer $375-550
   Cigar cutter $45-65
   Matchsafe $65-85
   Flask $175-250
   3 Flasks $175-250
   Tiffany flask $350-500

93-1 Rye bottle $350-400
   Kentucky Tavern $45-65
   Copper funnel $65-85
   2 Barrel $450-550
   Brookhill Whiskey $550-650
   etched beer glasses $20-35
   etched jiggers $10-25

94-1 Corkscrews $100-250
   2 Knife $25-45
   Little Giant $85-125
   Ornate corkscrew $125-175
   Ivory finial lime squeezer - Rare
   folding knife $85-125
   3 The Fairest Wheel $850-1250

95-1 Star Advertiser $850-1250

96-1 Trade stimulator $1000-1500
   2 Saloon painting - Rare

97-1 Cigar lighters $350-500
   2 Battery cigar lighters $250-350
   Nude cigar cutter - Rare
   3 Cigar lighters $250-350
   4 Cigar cutters $125-250
   Tobacco humidor $85-125

98-1 Dolly Madison $275-300
   2 Buffalo Lager $2000-2500

99-1 Quaker Maid $450-600
   2 Schantz-Thomas $1200-1400

100-1 Schlitz $1200-1400
   2 Olympia $1250-1500
   3 Napa City $1700-1900
   4 Rainier $1400-1600

101-1 Yuengling's $1200-1500
   2 Yale $900-1200
   3 Gambrinus tray $125-300
   4 Pabst $650-900
   5 Jas. E. Pepper $2500-3000
   6 G. W. Jones $900-1200

102-1 Royal Stag $175-250
   2 National $600-800
   3 Tip trays $50-125

103-1 Choisser Rye - Rare

## GAMBLING IN THE OLD WEST

108-1 Bowie knife - Rare
   Your deal $125-175

109-1 California dirks - Rare
   2 Unsigned push dagger $1250-2500
   Ivory poker chips $10-25
   "Pot" $125-175
   Knuckle duster $375-550
   Pharo cards $100-150

110-1 Case Keeper, broad range
   a Printed card faces $350-650
   b Hand painted card faces $500-1000
   c Handcarved card faces $1500-2500
   2 Dealing box, unsigned $250-350
   Dealing box, signed $400-750
   Pharo cards $100-150

   3 Layout, unsigned $600-750
   Layout, signed $750-1500

111-1 Roulette Wheel
   a 16 inch $225-375
   b 24 inch $750-1000
   c 32 inch $1500-2500

112-1 Red and Black $400-650

113-1 Broadside - Rare
   2 Diana $2500-5000

114-1 Broadside - Rare
   2 Gambling License - Rare

115-1 Keno Goose
   a Unsigned $400-650
   b Signed $650-850
   c Ivory trim $1000-1500
   d With Ivory balls - add $150-250

116-1 Wheels-of-Fortune
   a Small $350-500
   b Medium $750-1000
   c Large $2000-2500

117-1 Chuck-a-Luck Layout $400-600
   2 Chuck-a-Luck Cage
   a Small $125-175
   b Medium $150-250
   c Large $250-350

118-1 Ivory Dice Cups $125-250
   Matchsafe $65-85
   2 Dice Drop $250-350
   Hazard horn $175-350
   3 Dice cups $25-50

119-1 Corner rounder, unsigned $500-750
   Corner rounder, signed $1000-1500
   Card trimmer, unsigned $750-1000
   Card trimmer, signed $1500-2500

120-1 Bug $125-175
   2 Derringer $375-550

121-1 Steamboat cards $35-65
   2 Holdouts, unsigned $750-1000
   Holdouts, signed $1250-1750

## THE EXPRESS COMPANIES

125-1 Treasure box $750-1000

126-1 Reward poster $350-500
   2 Presentation rifle - Rare

127-1 Pat Garrett pass $350-400
   Common pass $35-50
   2 Reward poster $125-175

128-1 Smith and Wesson Schofields $450-650
   2 Shotgun $400-650

129-1 Letter $35-65
   2 Letter $50-75
   3 Sealing devices $65-85
   4 Wax seals
   a Coyote, California-set $150-200
   b Public Use seal $45-65
   c Wells Fargo seal $125-175

## FRONTIER HOLSTERS and BELTS

7-1 Dragoons, Texas style $300-350 pr.

8-1 1860 Army U. S. $80-100
   1885 U. S. holster $100-125
 2 Missouri skin-tight $40-50

9-1 Civilian unsigned $25-45
 2 Civilian signed $35-45

10-1 Catalogs $35-65

11-1 Unsigned combo $85-110

17-1 Signed Texas maker $100-125
 2 Signed Texas maker $200-250
 3 Signed Texas maker $75-85
 4 Signed Texas maker $100-125

18-1 Signed, excellent condition $110-145
 2 Signed, poor condition $50-65
 3 Signed Texas maker $100-125

19-1 Signed Texas maker $75-85
 2 Signed Texas maker $45-60
 3 Signed, altered $65-75
 4 Signed Texas maker $85-100

20-1 Signed, wrist holster $75-95
 2 Signed, semi-modern $35-40
 3 Signed, semi-modern $85-95

21-1 Signed, semi-modern $35-50
 2 Signed, semi-modern $35-40

22-1 Signed Texas maker $125-150
 2 Signed Texas maker $60-75
 3 Signed, damaged $50-65
 4 Signed, semi-modern $25-30

23-1 Signed, clip holster $35-40

24-1 Signed, semi-modern $65-75
 2 Signed Texas maker $50-65

25-1 Signed, semi-modern $90-110

26-1 Signed combo $280-350
 2 Signed Colorado maker $150-175
 3 Signed Colorado maker $125-150

27-1 Signed money belt $150-200

28-1 Signed combo $185-200
 2 Signed combo $185-200

29-1 Signed California style $180-225
 2 Signed Colorado maker $200-250

30-1 Signed, poor condition $50-85
 2 Signed, semi-modern $85-95
 3 Signed Colorado maker $90-110

31-1 Signed, semi-modern $25-35
 2 Signed Colorado maker $50-65
 3 Signed Colorado maker $100-135
 4 Signed belt $50-85

32-1 Saddle bag, holster $350-500

33-1 Signed California holster $150-200

34-1 California combo $150-175
 2 Unsigned combo, early $125-150
 3 Signed California holster $100-150

35-1 Unsigned California style $185-250
 2 Unsigned Dragoon $150-185
 3 Unsigned California style $125-135
 4 California combo $300-450

36-1 Unsigned California, early $400-650
 2 Signed, semi-modern $85-125

37-1 Signed Territorial, old $200-285

38-1 Signed Territorial, old $95-125
 2 Signed Montana, early $75-85
 3 Signed, new condition $400-550

39-1 Signed Buscadero, early $125-145

40-1 Signed, Utah $85-95

41-1 Signed semi-modern $25-35
 2 Signed, semi-modern $30-35

42-1 Signed $75-85

43-1 Signed Territorial $85-125
 2 Unsigned, but identifiable $50-65

44-1 Signed, matching $250-350
 2 Upper lined $85-95
   Lower plain $75-85
 3 Unsigned moneybelt $95-110
 4 Signed matching combo $350-400

45-1 Signed, semi-modern $100-125
 2 Signed Territorial combo $185-235
 3 Signed moneybelt combo $250-285

47-1 Signed combo $350-400
 2 Signed Territorial $75-100

48-1 Territorial $100-135
 2 Signed oddity $50-60
 3 Signed, semi-modern $50-60

49-1 Signed Nevada maker $65-75

50-1 Unsigned $45-55
 2 Signed shoulder $100-150
 3 Unsigned $40-50
 4 Unsigned $60-75

51-1 Indian beaded $150-200
 2 Mexican combo $75-95

52-1 Trade named combo $95-110
 2 Trade named $45-60
 3 Trade named $45-65
 4 Trade named combo $85-110

53-1 Trade named $45-65
 2 Trade named combo $85-100

54-1 Unsigned Sheriff's combo $80-100
 2 Clip holster $60-80

55-1 Inside pocket $30-40
 2 Nude, semi-modern $50-65
 3 Model "T" holster $45-55

 4 Model "A" $50-65
 5 Semi-modern $95-110
 6 Homemade combo $35-45

56-1 British $40-65
 2 Half pouch, unsigned $40-60
 3 Unsigned, recognizable $60-65
 4 Unsigned, studded $135-175

57-1 Bridgeport without gun $180-250

58-1 Homemade "boot top" $45-65
 2 Unsigned, ornamented $85-125

59-1 Unsigned, Texas combo $100-125
 2 Unsigned tooled design $45-55
 3 Unsigned studded combo $125-175
 4 Unsigned basket weave $80-95

60-1 Border style combo $135-165
 2 Bandolero $75-100

61-1 Rare $350-500

## SPURS

63-1 Chihuahua $65-85

64-1 Silver inlaid California $200-250
 2 Buermann $300-350
 3 O. K. $100-150

65-1 Jumbo O. K. $150-175
 2 Gal-leg $175-225
 3 Mint O. K. $175-200
 4 Silver spot $135-165
 5 Jumbo O. K. $150-175

66-1 Unique McChesney $200-250
 2 Gal-leg $225-275

67-1 Goose-neck $350-450
 2 Steer $325-375
 3 American eagle $235-265

69-1 Double mounted $250-300
 2 Bottle-opener $250-300
 3 Unusual $225-275
 4 C. P. Shipley $350-400
 5 Coins $225-275

70-1 Gal-leg Bischoff and Co., $450-650
 2 J. O. Bass $750-900

71-1 Boone $325-375
 2 Shop made $165-185

72-1 Card suit $225-275
 2 Gal-leg $250-300
 3 Silver inlaid $275-325
 4 Ricardo $200-250

73-1 K. B. and P. $250-300
 2 Miniatures - Rare

74-1 J. Fox $450-550
 2 Paddy Ryan style $225-275

75-1 Gal-leg $275-325
 2 Gal-leg $225-275
 3 Mexican $135-165

# OLD WEST
# ANTIQUES & COLLECTABLES

## Complimentary Price Guide

The value of antiques is of interest to most collectors. Unfortunately, establishing a fair market value for items which are both unique and rare is an extremely difficult task. To complicate matters further, prices vary from one part of the country to another.

This price guide attempts to give the collector a general idea of comparable values. ''Mint'' is a term found in many price guides to describe antiques found in new condition. Antiques in this condition are seldom found. For purposes of this price guide, the price ranges cover items found in very good to excellent condition, except where otherwise noted.

GREAT AMERICAN
PUBLISHING COMPANY

5513 Hwy. 290 W.
Austin, Texas 78735

22/94

# OLD WEST

## ANTIQUES & COLLECTABLES

*Fly's Gallery,*                    TOMBSTONE A. T.

# OLD WEST

## ANTIQUES & COLLECTABLES

GREAT AMERICAN
PUBLISHING COMPANY

Library of Congress Catalog No. 79-55858


ISBN: 0-934632-00-6

Printed by
Taylor Publishing Co.
Dallas, Texas

Additional Copies of This
Book May be Ordered From:
Great American Publishing Co.
5513 Hwy. 290 West
Austin, Texas 78735

# CONTENTS

# FRONTIER HOLSTERS AND BELTS

*John A. Kopec*

Beginning with the immigrants to our Western Frontier, the lawless, the lawmen, and ending with the cattlemen and cowboys, the story of the civilian Western Frontier holster is only beginning to emerge. This revolver holster, as much a vital and integral part of the old Westerner's gear as his revolver, has today become a seperate study, an area of concentrated research. The Western holster's design, construction and uses have become a researcher's bonanza. Our study deals with this seldom encountered bit of Americana, the Western Frontier holster, its makers and ramifications.

Though holsters and belts (rigs) continue to predominate the "old leather" collecting field because of their close association with the hand guns they held, other leather articles often associated with the cowboy and the West also continue to gain collector interest. We see gains in the popularity of collecting old saddles, chaps and riatas. Other cowboy-related memorabilia is rapidly becoming collectable, and it seems that anything old, associated with the American Frontier West is now collectable. Some of these items, because of their traceable origins are now prime collector items.

Vast amounts of revolvers began to make the scene just prior to and through the Civil War period. Though there were many manufacturers of revolvers during those early days, there can be no question that the Colt dominated the side-arm field. Though earliest Colt Paterson models were used to some extent on the frontier, the real impact was not felt until the big Dragoon came along in the 1850s. Later, because of improved metallurgy, the Dragoon was superceded by the M1849 Pocket and the M1851 Colt Navy revolvers. True, these larger caliber arms were initially military in their intent, yet the needs of the civilian frontier market were growing. Because these earliest revolvers required a means of protection from the elements as well as a means of mobility, holsters began to "make the scene" primarily with the military, but also as these revolvers became more and more plentiful, by the western saddlemakers who "outfitted" the civilian trade.

Paralleling the vast production of side-arms of the various manufacturers, we find that the western cow-towns, mining towns, and seacoast towns each had a saddler. No matter how small the town, it seemed to have its saddle shop. Of course a saddle shop then, when transportation was by means of a horse, could be likened to an automobile parts store today; a vital and necessary part of the economy of that day.

Revolver production at Colts' alone had reached almost 700,000 units by the turn of the century. True, many of these arms were for the military, but military arms soon have a way of becoming "surplus" and large amounts of the various makes of military arms were soon available on the open market.

To absolutely categorize definite patterns in the evolution of the Western Frontier holster would be folly, however there are certain characteristics of these holsters which tend to "speak" of their early or later association with a given revolver type and/or era of use. Unfortunately generalities must be used to some extent. As the makers of these holsters tried desperately to compete for the best possible product, they innovated and perfected their belts and holsters as time progressed to suit the civilian frontier needs.

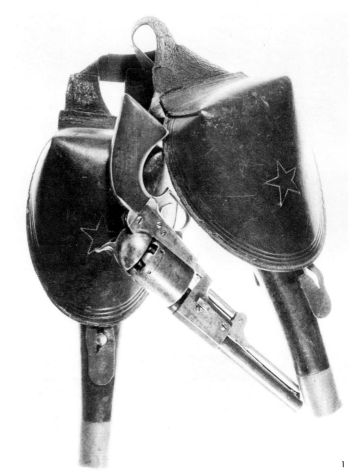

Earliest American handgun holsters were not worn on the waist, but were instead "pommel holsters" and were strapped in pairs over the pommel of the early Dragoon's saddle.

The Western pioneers' need for firearms has of course been covered by many writers. A vast wilderness of unsettled immigrants, communities, outlaws, Indians and wild animals provided the necessity for firearms, for protection, hunting and just plain survival. These firearms provided a measure of security which even today cannot be equalled in a near lawless society.

Progressing into our study of the Western Frontier holster, we find that the earliest "horse pistols" and Colt Dragoon varieties were not worn on the waist, but were securely holstered in pairs on the pommel of the Dragoon's saddle. These early hand-held arms were made quite cumbersome to assure a maximum fire power. This era of horse-ladened side arms continued in the military up through the early 1850's when we see the introduction of lighter more versatile revolvers like Colt's M1851, 36 caliber Navy. Earliest military records indicate that the reduced size "full-flap" navy holster was first issued with the purchase of the M1851 Navy Colts by the U.S. Navy. From this point, we begin to see two distinct lines of holster evolution; one the military, the other the civilian or "Western Frontier" holster, with which we concern ourselves in this study.

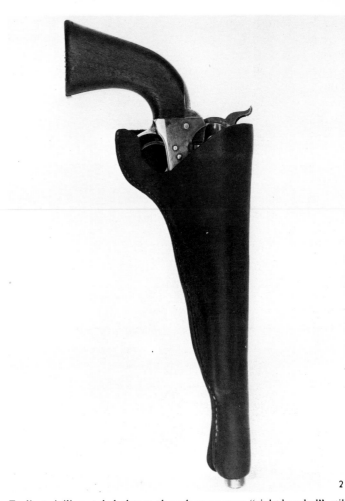

2

Earliest civilian style holsters, though some were "right handed", still retained a military silhouette. The "S" curve top pouch contour of the later "Frontier style" holsters begins to appear on the scene. This holster is for a Colt Richards Conversion of the M1860 Army revolver and remains very basic in design.

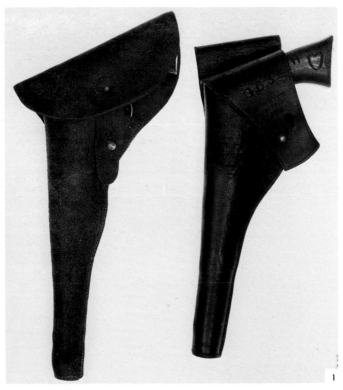

1

Earliest military waist belt holsters as issued with the M1851 Navy and the M1860 Army revolvers were of the "full flap" design (left illus.). This style was used through the Civil War and into the 1870's. During the Indian War period of the 1880's we see a modification known as the "half flap" design being employed by the military. This illustrated holster (right) is the M1885, and was issued with the Colt Single Action and S&W Schofield revolvers.

Again as we begin to study this "Western Frontier" holster we find that two general branches of the civilian variants are evident. These separate evolutionary categories again tend to parallel the firearms themselves.

Again we must reiterate that these are *general* categories and exceptions will always be found.

Though in many cases the earliest civilian used holsters were in fact only military holsters which may or may not have been modified by their owners, we see this military style or silhouette begin to be employed in the earliest trade holsters. These earliest trade holsters began to appear on the scene during the California Gold Rush when the migration to the West began. Colt's small M1849 pocket revolver and possibly some remaining Colt Paterson revolvers, along with many of the "infringement" or pepperbox revolvers were all popular and the "outfitters" were obliged to supply holsters for these various "pistols". Most of these earliest civilian holsters were in fact only scaled down versions of the "full flap" military holster. These served the westward bound travelers well, as they protected their percussion arms from the elements during the long journey.

As the West, and particularly California, began to be settled, saddle shops began to spring up in these western towns, and it is here where we see the beginnings of the true Western holster. These earliest civilian holsters were usually made for the Colt Percussion M1851 Navy revolver and were close-trimmed to contour to their respective revolver's silhouette. The "full flap" design of their military predecessors was abandoned and instead a pleasing "double S" curve of the leather profile finished the upper pouch contour. Interestingly these early examples in many cases retained the "left hand" crossdraw, butt forward, feature of their military counterparts. These earliest holsters are today termed by collectors the "California" or "Slim Jim" styles. In many instances these holsters were elaborately embellished with carvings and stampings of the period. Many show true California motifs like gold panners, and words like "Eureka". These "California style" holsters represent the earliest form of the true Western holster. Since their survival rate is extremely small, they are eagerly sought by today's collectors. Though these holsters of course fit well into a pure holster collection, they are not limited to this area. Any collection of Western Frontier memo-

This 19th Century gentleman sports his fine half-stock "Plains rifle" together with what appears to be a pair of M1875 Remington revolvers holstered in transitional civilian style holsters. Earliest civilian holsters resembled the Indian War's period military types with their flaps removed; however, in most cases these were not simply altered military holsters but were newly manufactured for the civilian trade. It is from these early transitional holsters that we find the "California style" holsters evolved.

Patterned along military lines, featuring a modified "full flap" design, this early civilian holster for a 7½" Colt S.A. sports a "bicycle chain" border and an early pattern "rosette". Though chronologically early in design and pattern, it was not necessarily made before the advent of the "California" or "Mexican loop" holsters. Many manufacturers continued to produce this style holster throughout their entire production period.

Again we see a modified "full flap" military-style civilian holster which would fit Colts M1877 Lightning or their M1895 "Swing-out" Navy revolvers. Simple in design, it features the military snap flap. It was manufactured in these early days to fit the countless numbers of small revolvers manufactured after the Civil War.

rabilia would welcome a "California" holster as it became an integral part of the Western story.

Though the early "California style" holsters were carried on a waist belt, this belt was usually quite narrow and had no cartridge loops, as was later the case when cartridges began to make the scene.

These early "California style" holsters continued in popularity throughout the West during the entire percussion era and into the Colt conversion period of the 1870's.

The second major division of Frontier holster evolution began with Colt's introduction of the Single Action Army or "peacemaker" in 1873. Though there are examples of transitional holsters, where the "slim Jim" style pouch is mounted onto a "Mexican style" skirt, these are few and far between and are considered scarce variants.

## The "Mexican Loop" Holster

The second and most popular collectable holster is called the "Mexican Loop". This style holster has had its name standardized by references throughout the many old, original catalogs we have been able to study. Though this holster's design probably originated in Old Mexico, its popularity quickly spread into the Old West and its style was complimented by the scores of saddle

makers who patterned their holsters after this unique and versatile configuration. This holster was made from a single piece of "oak tanned California Skirting leather". The pouch which held the revolver was fitted through a series of slits cut into the skirt which formed the loop or loops. The entire holster was made from only one piece of leather, and the main-seam was sewn with a waxed linen thread. Generally, we find that the shorter the holster the less loops it had, so a holster for a 4¾" Colt Single Action, almost always had only one loop, a holster for a 5½" Single Action may have had one or two loops, while a 7½" variant may have had two or three loops. Three-looped holsters are very scarce and are particularly attractive in design.

A second variant of the "Mexican Loop" though unclassified to date, must by reason of design be termed the "riveted loop" holster. Though it would be difficult to pinpoint the origins of this variant, it will have to be classified as very early and probably was synonymous in its era of production with the standard "Mexican Loop" variant dating well into the 1880's. This holster's construction featured the pouch and skirt patterned after the "Mexican Loop" variety, but the skirt was not slit to make the loops. Instead a separate piece of leather was riveted onto the skirt, usually with two, and sometimes four iron rivets. These iron rivets were either japanned or enameled to prevent rust and were used in

lieu of copper rivets which had been used on the earlier variants. These copper or brass rivets did not prove satisfactory as vertigris, the green residue which is formed on the rivets found on most old military holsters, often formed unsightly deposits. The iron rivets actually held up very well as enough oil seemed to be present in the leather to prevent their rusting. Their japanned or enameled coating just seemed to enhance their appearance, although this coating undoubtedly also contributed to their preservation.

A slight modification is also found in the "riveted loop" variant, and in this instance we find that only one end of the loop is riveted, while the other, and exposed end, is sewn to the skirt. Variants may also be found in which the entire loop is sewn and no rivets are employed. The earliest mentioned variant will be termed "riveted & sewn" loop or if no rivets are used, will be termed simply to have a "sewn loop" in this study.

Though a few authors have expounded on several variants of the "Mexican Loop" holster such as the "Denver Loop", "Border Loop", "Kansas Loop", and others, none of these terms were found to be used in the old catalogs which we have examined. To say the least their definitions are too vague to have any practical application to the collector of today, who prefers to have descriptive terminology. When a collector refers to a "Mexican Loop" holster with three loops the description will be clearly understood. When a "riveted loop" holster with one loop is mentioned the description can easily be determined to describe a single configuration. Since the study of the "Frontier Holsters" is yet in its infancy, we are sure that clearer definitions will yet evolve. Types may be categorized into more definite patterns, but for now the reader can be assured of at least two major classifications, with possibly two subclassifications of the "Mexican Loop" holster. It must be reiterated that because of extreme variances, absolutes can only be established on a minimal level.

Besides the basic variants of the "Mexican Loop" holsters which we have just covered, there are two rather distinct variants which should be mentioned and classified.

## The "Cheyenne"

Our study of these early holster forms reveals that a unique variant of the "Mexican Loop" holster was manufactured in the early days in the Wyoming and Montana areas. This type of holster had a "tear-drop" muzzle plug, which for some reason has become a characteristic appreciated by today's collectors. Leading the field of these "Cheyenne" holsters are those manufactured by Frank Meanea, though other makers in this area such as E.L. Gallatin and Eldred and Morrow also incorporated this feature into their holsters. The "Dutchman" W.B. Ten Eyck of Billings, Montana Territory also incorporated this "teardrop" muzzle plug

1

into his holsters. Other makers offered a "muzzle plug" at an additional charge, but generally it was regarded as a hinderance as accumulated debris could be trapped within the holster. We believe the reason for the extensive use of the muzzle plug in these Northern Territories was to eliminate the possible injection of snow into the holster, and hence the revolvers muzzle when the wearer fell or possibly sat in the snow.

## A Texas "Jock-Strap" Variant

For lack of a better name, and because examples of this variant seem to have originated in the Lone Star State, we've labeled this one the "Texas Jock-Strap" style. Though the basic design still remains the "Mexican Loop", this holster's loop has been modified in design to wrap not only the front circumference of the pouch, but to also neatly wrap around the muzzle area. The characteristic shape of this modified loop, which looks much like a "jock-strap" incorporates a very practical method of reinforcing stress areas of these holsters. Several Texas makers have manufactured holsters of

this style; among these being H.A. Holtzer and S.D. Myers. Though exceptions are bound to be found, our observations indicate this to be a localized pattern adopted by these few Texas makers.

## The Western Holster as an Art Form

We would like to suggest the collector's consideration of the "Frontier Holster" as a true form of American Frontier Art. There can be no question that the individualism and simplicity of design employed in these early holsters, let alone their endemic embellishments, border designs, rosettes, and silhouettes, be seriously considered and appreciated as a form of "Frontier Art". The pride of construction, design and adornment is exemplified in these old holsters. "Signed" variants of course were "living" advertisements for their manufacturers and it was observed again and again that each saddler repeatedly stated his product was "superior to any other". The pride of quality prevailed and this quality

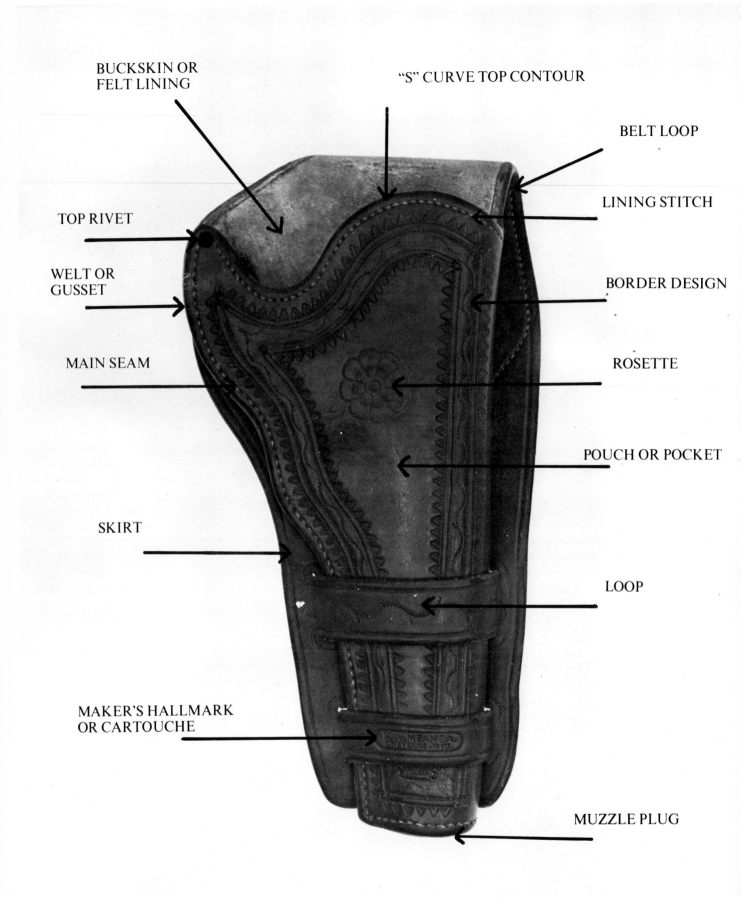

BUCKSKIN OR
FELT LINING

"S" CURVE TOP CONTOUR

BELT LOOP

TOP RIVET

LINING STITCH

WELT OR
GUSSET

BORDER DESIGN

MAIN SEAM

ROSETTE

POUCH OR POCKET

SKIRT

LOOP

MAKER'S HALLMARK
OR CARTOUCHE

MUZZLE PLUG

**NOMENCLATURE.** Common terms used to describe the various parts, characteristics, or markings found on a typical Western "Mexican Loop" holster. Some of these terms are old, others are quite new and descriptive. Most are in use throughout this text to describe the characteristics of the illustrated holsters to follow.

resulted in keen competition which seems to have been lost on the American scene. Holsters then, as an "Art Form" can and must be appreciated for their sheer beauty, simplicity of design, and as being manufactured at the pinnacle of the then thriving leathercraft industry.

# "Mexican Loop" Holster Nomenclature

Along with a study of the holsters, their respective makers and characteristic styles, some simple standardization of the terms in use to describe the various parts of a holster are in order. We have prepared a chart which shows and names many of these collector-important characteristics of the "Mexican Loop" holster. Though we have illustrated a typical holster, it should be pointed out that not all "Mexican Loop" holsters display all of these characteristics. There are, however, several which incorporate the basic pattern; these being the pouch, the skirt, the loops, the "S" curve top-pouch contour, and the main seam. Other minor and often encountered characteristics are shown in the accompanying illustration and need not be repeated here. Innovations like thong stitching, snaps, safety straps, laced loops, leg thongs, hammer thongs and basket-weave designs are considered as being modern or semi-modern in design, and holsters having any of these characteristics will only be included on a minimal basis in this study. The western movie "Buscadero" rig will only be included in one instance in this work as these are not generally considered to be products of the true Western Frontier.

# Money Belts, Cartridge Belts and Buckles

The cartridge belt, of course, had to begin with the cartridge revolver. Earliest attempts to make belts with suitable loops to carry cartridge supplies originated with the military who experimented with leather loops and finally settled on the use of the "woven cartridge belt" which prevailed during the Indian and Spanish American War eras. Civilian cartridge belts evolved during this same period but the use of leather loops was generally acceptable, with only a few instances where the "Mills Pattern" woven cartridge belts were used in connection with rifle ammunition. There seems to be some conjecture that if leather which was used in these belts was the "Oak tanned" California type, that deposits of verdigris from the reaction between the brass cartridges and the leather would be eliminated.

Cartridge belts were manufactured by many of the same manufacturers or saddlers who furnished the holsters. Loops were in most cases sewn in position and hand-stitching demanded a premium over the machine stitched belts. Loops were also riveted in position, laced with raw hide, or woven through appropriately spaced slots in the belts. Cartridge belts were available in several widths and buckle styles. Money belts were available in 3 inch, 3½ inch and 4 inch widths, with a single or double row of cartridge loops. These money belts contained a special slit or open end through which gold coins or silver dollars could be inserted. When the billet of the belt was inserted through this slit and into the buckle the coins would be safely locked into the inner fold of the belt. These money belts were made of folded calfskin, one piece, stitched at the top. So a three inch combination cartridge and money belt was made from a six-inch wide piece of calf skin. Collectors today eagerly seek the old style cartridge money belts. They are extremely desirable, especially with two rows of cartridge loops and with the maker's "cartouche" or hallmark. The typical square or rectangular nickel buckles with their corners cropped, generally found on these old cartridge belts were termed "California style" or "long pattern nickel California belt buckles."

The H.H. Heiser Co. of Denver seemed to specialize in these cartridge belts and featured the belts made of "Medium Weight California Oak tanned skirting leather". These belts featured thirty ¾ inch cartridge loops sewn in. They were available in "all plain", "Full hand bullseye stamped" or "Mexican hand raised carved finish". Their "Combination Cartridge and Money Belt" was made of "chrome tanned Chaparejo leather", "which is very soft and tough and not affected by perspiration. Money could not be withdrawn unless the billet was withdrawn from the buckle. Original price for the three inch money belt was $5.50.

Collectors today generally accept the fact that only in a few instances have belts and holsters (rigs) been found to match. This is to say that both belt and holster were manufactured by the same "maker", and if not identified by a maker's name, that these two units match in style, workmanship and design. Of course, when real matching "rigs" are encountered they are considered very rare and desirable by today's standards.

# Construction Materials

Repeated references to "Oak Tanned California Skirting Leather" are found in the old saddler's and holster manufacturer's catalogs. Evidently this material became the standard from which these holsters were manufactured. The Heiser catalogs however refer to an "extra-heavy Oak Tanned California Skirting Leather", and observation of Heiser's old holsters bear this fact out as the majority of these observed holsters are "tempered", the leather being extremely tough and stiff, form-molded to fit a precise model revolver.

Western Frontier holsters are found lined in some cases with "buck skin" lining. Sometimes they are found with red or blue felt lining. Though these felt-lined holsters were probably constructed with the guns' finish in mind, they in reality helped to rapidly reduce the revolvers' finish when the felt became filled with sand and grit.

Harper & Co.,  2215 Market Street, GALVESTON.  920 Congress Ave., AUSTIN, TEX.

## Saddlery Shops

In most cases it was the town's saddler who manufactured the cowboy's leather needs. Some of these shops were small, while others became large factories which employed many workers. Interestingly, and quite American was the aspect that these shops were "family affairs". Most were passed on from father to son for several generations, while "branch operations" were begun in outlying towns by nephews. Many smaller shops were bought out when a more prosperous owner decided to expand. This is why we find references to the same maker or a joint-partnership springing up in several locations. Custom work prevailed. Holsters were always made to "fit the gun" and exact barrel lengths

and model specifications were required with each order. Right- and left-handed holsters were available in each style. Custom lining, muzzle plugs, conchos and studding were available at extra cost. Cartridge belt loops could be added at 5¢ per loop additional charge. Though several writers have suggested that the saddlers were found along the "Texas Trails" this may be true to a certain extent, but in reality these shops were not restricted to any given area. They were located all over the West. Without doubt, most saddlers and holster makers were, however, found in Texas. Texas was the center of the cattle industry, so there were more "cow punchers" there and consequently a greater market. Colorado vied for the next most popular manufacturing area, while California took third place. Most of the other Western states were represented as having holster-producing saddle shops.

## Hallmarked Holsters

Only about one out of every ten old "Mexican Loop" holsters encountered today will be found with the maker's hallmark, or "Cartouche" as the collectors like to refer to this stamping. Since holsters having these cartouches represented a maker's best effort, it also signified his sense of pride in the finished product. Collectors today appreciate these "signed" holsters and belts to a much greater degree than the "unsigned" variants. The signature usually is followed by the word "MAKER" and the city or town, state or territory in which the saddler worked. Those old holsters which were manufactured in the territories and are marked "A.T." (Arizona Terr.), "I.T." (Indian Terr.), "M.T." (Montana Terr.), or "O.T." (Oklahoma Terr.) are especially desirable collector items because of their traceable origins. Since the study of saddlery shops and the collecting of holsters is still in its infancy, we will only list the names and addresses of the makers which we have observed in the short time allotted us for this presentation. Each one of these individual "MAKERS" represents a challenge for research to the prudent student. Each saddle shop can be researched through old catalogs, old city directories or historical societies, and each one can tell its own story. Only recently have we begun to see this sort of research on the individual saddlery begin to emerge. It is hoped that this humble work will encourage others to pursue a line of research and study regarding their particular hallmarked holster. Fascinating facts can be found, living descendants interviewed and observations published. It is even possible to stumble onto a picture of an unidentified "unsigned" holster in an old saddler's catalog. This was the one with the "N. Porter" holster which is "unsigned" yet was identified beyond any doubt in their old catalog, and is illustrated in this section.

"Unsigned" holsters are without doubt very much apreciated by collectors, but their origins are obscure. Catalog searching may, in some cases, prove rewarding and an "unsigned" holster may be identified. We feel that the basic designs of the "signed" holsters represented in this book, would more than likely cover the basic designs of the majority of unsigned holsters the collector might encounter. For this reason we are concentrating on the presentation of as many "signed" examples as we have been able to locate prior to the publication of this work. We are by no means belittling the unsigned varieties and find them as interesting and colorful as the signed ones, and have devoted a portion of this study to them. Several of the holsters which are in our own personal collection are of the unsigned types.

## Determining Desirability

What factors determine one given holster or holster/belt combination to be more collector-desirable than another? The first factor which would determine desirability would be "Character". Does the holster and/or belt look like it had been used for many years on the frontier? Does it display its original embellishments and designs? Does it show a prominent maker's cartouche? Is its maker from an old Western cowtown, mining town or rail center? Was it made in a Territory? Are the markings clear and readable? Are there rips or tears in the leather? Are the seams sound? Is the leather in good condition? These are but a few of the various factors which become the criteria on which a collector can base a buying or selling price. Holsters which were made by well known makers also have a special appeal. Holsters with historical significance, or which have belonged to famous lawmen or outlaws have particular appeal, but their documentation must be foolproof! Though the "unsigned" or unidentifiable holsters far outnumber those which are "signed" with the maker's cartouche, they are still very desirable collectors items if they do not show the several "semi-modern" characteristics, like snap straps or basket weave designs. Collectors must learn to spot these characteristics to make their own determinations. Semi-modern holsters also seem to break away somewhat from the old traditional maker's cartouche. Many are simply stamped with the maker's name and the work "MAKER" has been eliminated as well as the traditional encircled cartouche. It was this distinctive cartouche which had become a standard method of identification on the pre-1900 manufactured holsters. Basically, what we are talking about is "feel" for a holster, its character and desirability, which only comes from experience. You can use some of the guidelines outlined in this section, and they most assuredly will help. But experience is still the best teacher after all.

Progressing further into the factors which determine value, there are several other criteria on which a determination can be made.

A very important factor is age. Those holsters which were made before 1900 are considerably more desirable than those which we term "semi-modern". The holsters which were made for the 7½" Colt Single Action seem to appeal to collectors to a greater degree than those of a shorter length. Holsters which are hallmarked with the maker's name and are from an old Western area like Texas, Colorado, or Wyoming, seem to have greater appeal. Matching belts also tend to at least double the value of a "rig" while matching money belts may even triple the value. Semi-modern "Hollywood" or "Buscadero" rigs are seldom considered collectable by today's collector. These may fit well into a movie museum but are really not part of the Old West.

# Fakes

It is with a note of sadness that we must report on this topic. As the value of any antique begins to soar the larceny in men's hearts begins to be revealed. We have recently observed newly made "Mexican style" holsters manufactured from old leather! These, of course, are detectable to the trained collector, but what about the beginning collector? Will he get burned? These "fakes" are easily spotted because the cuts of the leather appear new. There is however a new form of fakery which is now beginning to surface which will be even tougher to spot. This form of fakery has been going on in the gun collecting hobby for years. This fakery is probably best termed "upgrading". An original old "unsigned" Mexican loop holster is upgraded by the addition of a maker's cartouche! This will of course enhance its value to the unsuspecting collector two or three fold. The only advice which we can offer is to carefully examine the maker's cartouche to see if it appears to look newer than the rest of the holster. Check, if possible, the holster against other known examples of this same maker's products to see if construction traits match. Finally, *know* from whom you purchase the holster, and if a doubt is present, get a written money back guarantee. We understand that these maker's cartouches are being applied to holsters using well-known and respected makers' names. Buyer beware!

# Holster "MAKERS"

It is generally accepted that the holster and belt business was simply a by-product of the local saddlery shop. In most cases this was the case and few saddlers offered more than a half dozen holster styles. There are of course exceptions to this rule; one of which was the H.H. Heiser concern of Denver. Although they are called "saddlers" their later catalogs show no saddles, but they specialize in holsters, rifle scabbards, and other small leather goods.

Since we believe that the story of the various makers, their locations and their period of business is yet to be told in its entirety, we will attempt to list those few makers whom we have located or their products observed, by the states in which they were located. Brief comments will be made on individual makers where this material is available. Others will be simply listed, with no comment, and in some cases examples of their holsters illustrated. It is hoped that this brief study will encourage others to make greater contributions in this field. The states with the most makers are listed first, in order of diminishing amounts.

# Texas

It is not surprising that the "Lone Star State" would be first with the greatest representation of saddle shops. Texas was cattle country and the cowboy prevailed. Though we are listing twenty-nine Texas makers up through the depression period, we feel that many new Texas makers will be uncovered in the figure:

**E.T. Amonett,** El Paso, Tex. Closed shop in 1920; moved to Roswell, New Mexico.

**Charles Bluemel,** El Paso, Tex. Past 1920, opened shop when E.T. Amonett closed. Son Charles still in business.

**A.W. Brill,** Austin, Tex. Cartouche noted on a 4¾" S.A. Mexican Loop holster.

**W.H. Clay,** Brownsville, Tex.

**J.F. Dunn Saddlery,** San Angelo, Tex.

**E.B. Elam,** San Antonio, Tex.

**L. Frank,** San Antonio, Tex.

**El Paso Saddlery,** El Paso, Tex. Moved to Overland and Oregon Street (corner) in 1901. Went out of business in 1902.

**P. Gessler,** Pecos, Tex.

**R.E. Gibbons,** Gainesville, Tex.

**A.H. Hess,** Houston, Tex.

**Hobby Harness Co.,** Waco, Tex.

**H.A. Holtzer,** Llano, Tex. Established before 1903. Holtzer died in 1917.

**W.E. Lutz,** Bastrop, Tex.

**Newton Porter:** Taylorville, Tex. Holster marked: "N. Porter, Taylorville, Tex". Established in Taylorville in 1875, moved to Abilene, Tex. in 1888 and to Phoenix, Arizona Territory in 1895. Newton Porter died in 1906, and the firm was managed by his eldest son, Earl. Mail order business prospered and a branch was opened in Scottsdale by a cousin, Wm. N. Porter (see Arizona listing)

**Preston-Martin,** Del Rio, Tex.

**S.D. Myers,** El Paso, Tex. The S.D. Myers Saddle Co. began business in 1893 in Sweetwater, Tex., and was one of the most widely known and respected saddlers of all time. They moved to El Paso in 1920. The owner "Teo Sam" as he was affectionately known made his famous holsters for such personages as General George S. Patton, Will Rogers, Pancho Villa, Lazarno Cardenas, Col. J.C. Miller, John R. Hughes, and Gene Autry. "Teo Sam" passed away on July 2, 1953. Business continued after "Teo Sam's" death by his son Bill and nephew Dance.

**Padget Bros. Co.,** Dallas, Tex.

**Newton and Andrews,** El Paso, pre 1886 listing.

**C.L. Rogers,** Stamford, Tex.

**A.F. Schlick,** Wharton, Tex.

**Sheldon-Payne,** El Paso, circa. 1894.

**M.A. Smith,** Albany, Tex.

**Stelzig Saddlery,** Houston, Tex.

**Theo. Steubing,** San Antonio, Tex.

**E. Tackabar,** Fort Worth, Tex.

**G.H. Tips,** Houston, Tex.

**Ben Varga,** Established 1854, passed from father to son for four generations. Fakes have been noted.

**Hy B. Verhelle,** Brownsville, Tex.

1

2

E. T. Amonett, maker, El Paso. This "riveted and sewn" Mexican loop holster for a 4¾″ Colt Single Action was manufactured prior to 1920, when this shop was moved to Roswell, New Mexico. A neatly tooled floral and border pattern covers the pouch. The maker's cartouche is located on the right skirt.

W. H. Clay, Brownsville, Texas. This neatly made holster is buckskin lined and fits a Colt 7½″ Single Action. It sports two "riveted and sewn" loops. The entire holster is nicely tooled and studded. The extra stitching in various locations secures the lining on this example. Maker's cartouche is on the upper pouch.

3

4

L. Frank, maker, San Antonio. A single loop Mexican style holster for a 4¾″ Colt SA sports a short squared-off skirt. Hand tooled throughout representing a rather unique styling.

E. B. Elam, maker, San Antonio, Texas. This modified "Mexican loop" holster sports the "riveted and sewn" single loop with the maker's hallmark, eliminates the "S" curve upper pouch contour, and is stitched closed at the muzzle. The holster's pouch has about a ¾″ welt sewn into the main-seam. The money-belt with this holster sports the "long-pattern California style buckle." Both show nice old tooling designs of the Mexican style.

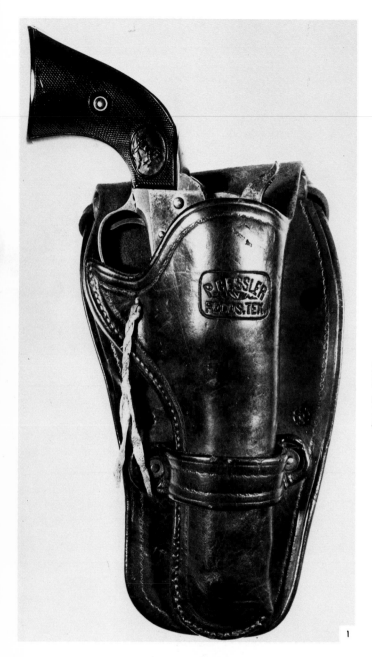

El Paso Saddlery, El Paso. A plain holster for a 5½″ Colt S.A. Mexican style with a riveted loop. Maker's cartouche is plainly visible at the top of the pouch. The barrel seems to have worn through the muzzle end and a reinforcing rivet added. The belt, a single-stitched money belt was manufactured by Shelton-Payne of El Paso.

A very early example of a Pete Gessler holster in the "gunfighter" barrel length of 4¾″. Pecos, Texas was known as a re-outfitting and "cooling-off" place for many of the notorious gunfighters that operated around El Paso. Date of manufacturer is estimated circa 1890-1910. Note use of the "riveted loop", the tiny "rosettes" on the skirt, and the late use of copper rivets.

R. E. Gibbons, Gainesville, Texas. A wide looped Colt S.A. holster. Loop is stitched onto the skirt. A simple line design, with rosette at the border junctions is used. Rosette design also decorates the upper pouch. The maker's cartouche is deeply stamped onto the extra wide loop.

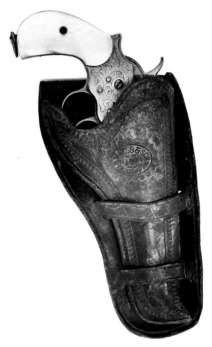

A. H. Hess and Son, maker, Houston, Texas. A true "Mexican loop" style holster for a 5½″ Colt, double looped, simple border design with rosettes at the border junctions. Maker's name in a cartouche is marked "A. H. Hess & Son". A typical, but desirable Texas made holster.

A. H. Hess & Co., maker, Houston, Texas. Possibly made after 1900, this holster is fitted with a saw-toothed belt clip. A simple pouch type holster for a 4¾″ Colt S.A. A zig-zag border design showing a distinct maker's cartouche. An early "gentleman's" holster.

H. A. Holtzer, Llano, Texas. A unique "riveted and sewn" Texas "jock-strap" variant showing this feature well. The loop sports a simple linked circle pattern, with three tiny rosettes placed onto the pouch and lower loop. The upper pouch contour and hammer thong are probably later modifications.

Another fine example of an H. A. Holtzer holster. This one though similar to the previous illustrated example does not show the rivets on the loop, while it does show a slightly different pattern design. The "rosettes" of the previous holster have been substituted by "sunburst" designs.

An S. D. Myers hideaway wrist gambler's rig made for a Remington double derringer. An innovation and a "signed" piece of Americana.

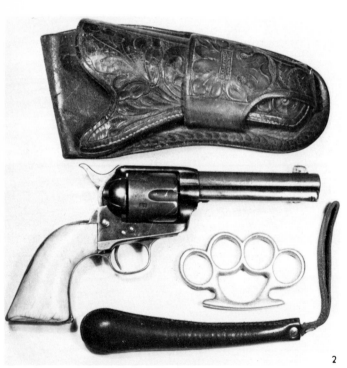

2

S. D. Myers Saddlery Co., El Paso, Texas. A hand tooled Texas "jock-strap" style holster beautifully deep hand tooled and well constructed. This holster, revolver, and other "persuaders" were all used by Sheriff Reeder Webb of Ector Co., Texas, 1923-1941.

3

W. E. Lutz, Bastrop, Texas. A black, narrow skirted, wrap-around looped holster for a 4¾″ Single Action. Skirt is sewn to the muzzle and some repair work is evident. A reinforced pouch contour has been added. Maker's name remains very distinct on the loop.

A classic example of an S. D. Myers, Texas "jock-strap" style holster, left handed, beautifully executed, probably was originally part of a "Buscadero Rig". The upper pouch "S" curve seems to be exaggerated, as it envelopes nearly the entire upper portion of the pouch.

2

1

Padgett Bros. Co., makers, Dallas, Texas. This holster for a 4¾" Colt S.A. has a light lined tooled border with a rosette at each junction of the border design. Russet color, this holster has a unique strap which fits diagonally behind the hammer and across the trigger guard area. Maker's cartouche is located on the lower skirt. A simple tooled 1½" wide loop is sewn into place on the skirt.

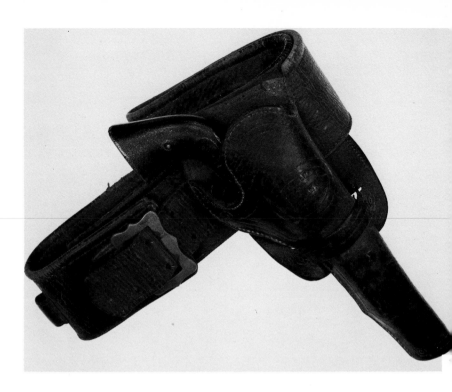

Made by E. Tackabar of Fort Worth, this rig departs from the usual Mexican style in that the holster's pouch is very contoured and reminiscent of a California or "slim-jim" Type, while the skirt is only half length and only one loop is employed. Also, note the lines of the "S" curve top pouch contour! The accompanying money belt's buckle is also very unique, and one of the fanciest we've seen.

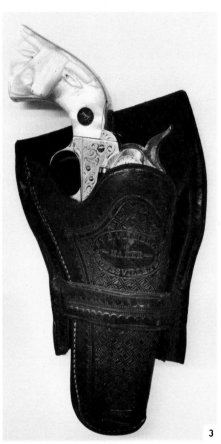

Shelton-Payne, El Paso, Texas. W. H. Payne and W. H. Shelton formed the Shelton-Payne Arms Co. in 1901. They were located at 305 N. Oregon St., El Paso. Shelton was a former partner in the El Paso Saddlery. This holster is for a 4¾" Colt S.A. It is made of black leather, the loop is riveted in place with two copper rivets. Cartouche is located on the lower right skirt.

Hy B. Verhelle made this one in Brownsville. Typically a "Mexican Loop" it incorporates a wide skirt, which may have originally had two loops. Maker's cartouche is prominently displayed on the pouch's center; nicely hand tooled with typical "rosettes" at the border design's junctions.

C. L. Rogers, Stamford, Texas. A neatly made semi-modern basket weave design holster with a very narrow skirt and a single, wide sewn loop. The loop displays the maker's cartouche. A pleasant very gradual "S" curve top pouch contour adds to the eye appeal of this 4¾" Colt Single Action holster.

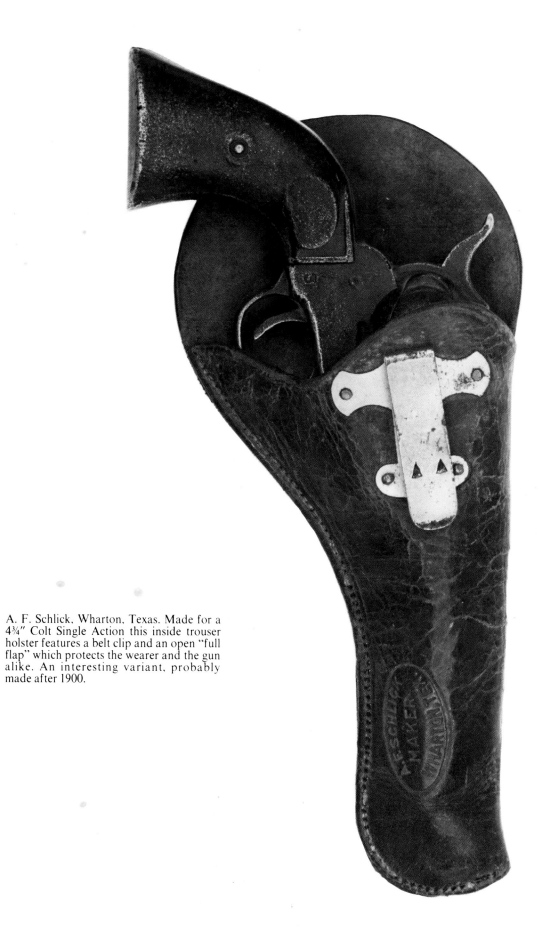

A. F. Schlick, Wharton, Texas. Made for a 4¾″ Colt Single Action this inside trouser holster features a belt clip and an open "full flap" which protects the wearer and the gun alike. An interesting variant, probably made after 1900.

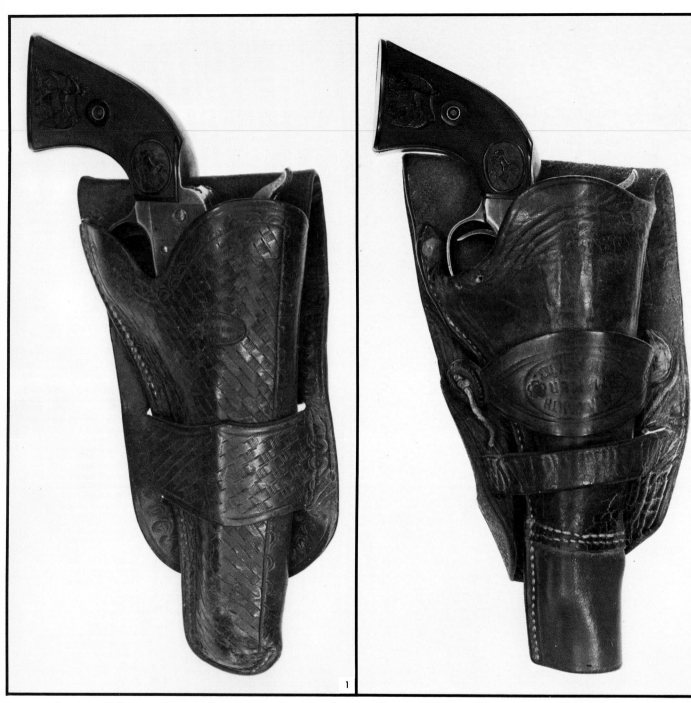

1

2

A very well constructed, heavy duty, single wide loop Mexican style holster made by Theodore Steubing of San Antonio. The basket weave design hints of a more modern construction, nevertheless, a very nice holster. Ox blood in color, the patterns are well executed.

M. A. Smith, maker, Albany, Texas. A very unique single-loop Mexican style holster for a Colt S.A. short skirt, with the maker's cartouche attached by means of a special loop originally knotted in place with rawhide thongs and leather conchas. Cartouche loop is now affixed up-side down. A copper rivet reinforces the top main seam.

# Colorado Makers

The second state representing the greatest number of holster manufacturers is Colorado. Colorado is noted for its mining towns, and therefore, we hope that the holsters here will reflect this influence. Collectors immediately will recognize some of the greatest names as being Colorado "Makers". Greats among those are R.T. Frazier, Pueblo; E.L. Gallatin, S.C. Gallup and H.H. Heiser, all of Denver.

**W.D. Allison,** Montrose, Colo; Purchased the original (1883) Charles Swope Saddlery from M.E. French in 1911.

**P. Becker,** Leadville, Colo.

**Ike Cherry,** Durango, Colo; circa 1887.

**Denver Mfg. Co.,** Denver, Colo.

**Frazier & Flynn,** a partnership circa 1921.

**M.E. French,** Montrose, Colo. purchased the original Charles Swope Saddlery.

**Thomas Flynn,** Silver Cliff, Colo., circa 1880, later moved to Trinidad, Colo. and then to Pueblo in 1882. Remained in business thru 1935.

**R.T. Frazier,** Pueblo, Colo. "The largest manufacturers of high grade saddles in the World" is so stated in the R.T. Frazier catalog #22. One of the best known saddlers probably began his career during the 1870's with P. Becker in Leadville, later he worked with Gallup and soon became a partner. After about ten years R.T. Frazier Saddlery Co. was established in the 1880's. His well known slogans like "The Cowboy Saddle Capital" put the city of Pueblo on the map. R.T. Frazier died in the mid 1920's.

**E.L. Gallatin & Co.,** Denver; Began in 1863. In 1864 moved to Virginia City, Montana Territory. In 1866 S.C. Gallup purchased one-half interest and the firm was re-named Gallup & Gallatin. A branch was opened in Nebraska City, Nebraska in 1867, and another shop opened in Cheyenne, Wyoming in 1873. The Cheyenne shop was sold to Frank Meanea upon Gallatin's retirement in 1873.

**S.C. Gallup,** Pueblo, Colo., circa 1870 thru 1930.

**Francis Gallup,** Denver, Colo. Purchased the Denver operation of the Gallatin & Gallup Saddlery in 1873.

**Gallup & Frazier,** Pueblo, Colo. Listed in the "Big Four Brand Book" for 1897.

**Greyhound Specialty Co.,** Denver, Colo.

**Charles Hammond,** Delta, Colo., Circa 1885.

**Herman H. Heiser,** Denver, Colo. This is one of the "big ones". Hermann H. Heiser came to Platterville, Wisconsin in 1849 from Germany. Later he moved to Central City, Colorado and still later to Denver. He began his shop there in the Spring of 1858. It grew to be one of the largest and most respected holster manufacturing firms of the nation. His motto was "No man ever lived long enough to wear out a Heiser holster." Holsters were a specialty, and his later catalogs show no saddles being manufactured. His holsters were made of either "Oak tanned California Skirting leather" or "Extra heavy selected California Saddle leather". Heiser died in 1903, but the business continued under the direction of his son Ewald until 1945. Keystone Bros. merger, 1944.

**Peter Hirsh,** Denver, Colo.

**Fred Mantey,** Grand Junction, Colo., circa 1885.

**E.H. Metz,** Colorodo Springs, Colo., Circa 1890.

**Fred Mueller,** Denver, Colo., Circa 1883. Located on Larimer Street. Mueller retired in 1917 but the business continued. Their catalog of July 1, 1935 lists only two holsters, a "Double loop" and a "Single Wide loop" with an extra wide skirt.

**Lenord Scheck Saddle Co.,** Denver, Colo.

**Charles Swope,** Montroese, Colo., Circa 1883.

**W.R. Thompson,** Rifle, Colo. Circa 1888, Died in 1908. Shop continued into the 1930's.

**Western Saddle Mfg. Co.,** 1651 Larimer Street, Denver, Colo. Catalog 55 for 1938, page 72 shows an extra wide skirted, basket-weave patterned holster, straight top pouch, with a double loop, a large oval "cartouche" is located at the top of the pouch.

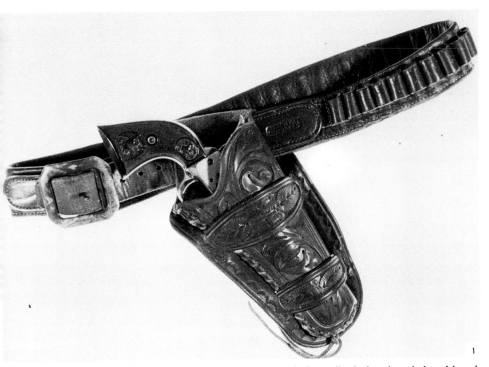

R. T. Frazier made this fine double looped Mexican style holster, finely hand tooled and laced. The main-seam, however, was re-wrapped in this example. A matching "Frazier" money belt makes this a great combination rig. Back side of this holster is marked "property U.S. Marshals Office, Denver".

An R. T. Frazier manufactured double matching rig for a 7½″ Colt Single Action. Without doubt this rig would vie for one of the finest outfits represented in this book. The massive size and weight alone of such a rig fully loaded would be impressive. Note the super wide skirts and simplicity of design as well as the decorative rosettes.

Listed as R. T. Frazier's #3205 holster, this one is described in their catalog #22 as having "Fair leather, buckskin sewn, silver trimmed with buttons and Conchas to match our #4200 chaps". Price $5.25.

Denver Manufacturing Co. An extra nice "Mexican loop" holster for a 7½″ Colt Single Action reflects the cattle industry's influence on the leather trade. The extra wide loops are nicely marked with a cow's head and the maker's cartouche. The "S" cruve top pouch contour has been modified by the addition of a gore. Main seam also shows some later reinforcements.

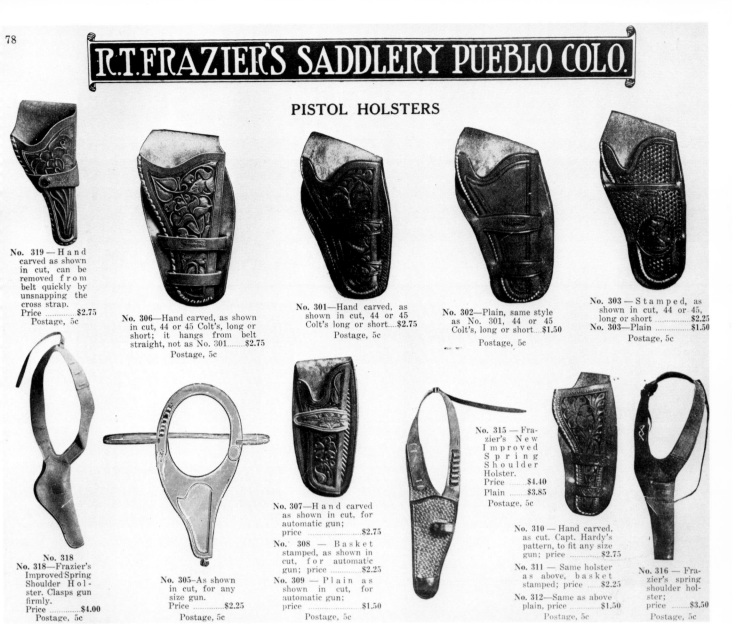

# R.T. FRAZIER'S SADDLERY PUEBLO COLO.

## PISTOL HOLSTERS

**No. 319**—Hand carved as shown in cut, can be removed from belt quickly by unsnapping the cross strap. Price ............ $2.75 Postage, 5c

**No. 306**—Hand carved, as shown in cut, 44 or 45 Colt's, long or short; it hangs from belt straight, not as No. 301......$2.75 Postage, 5c

**No. 301**—Hand carved, as shown in cut, 44 or 45 Colt's long or short....$2.75 Postage, 5c

**No. 302**—Plain, same style as No. 301, 44 or 45 Colt's, long or short....$1.50 Postage, 5c

**No. 303**—Stamped, as shown in cut, 44 or 45, long or short ............$2.25 **No. 303**—Plain ............$1.50 Postage, 5c

**No. 318**
**No. 318**—Frazier's Improved Spring Shoulder Holster. Clasps gun firmly. Price ............$4.00 Postage, 5c

**No. 305**—As shown in cut, for any size gun. Price ............$2.25 Postage, 5c

**No. 307**—Hand carved as shown in cut, for automatic gun; price ....................$2.75 **No. 308**—Basket stamped, as shown in cut, for automatic gun; price ............$2.25 **No. 309**—Plain as shown in cut, for automatic gun; price ............$1.50 Postage, 5c

**No. 315**—Frazier's New Improved Spring Shoulder Holster. Price ............$4.40 Plain ............$3.85 Postage, 5c

**No. 310**—Hand carved, as cut. Capt. Hardy's pattern, to fit any size gun; price ............$2.75 **No. 311**—Same holster as above, basket stamped; price ............$2.25 **No. 312**—Same as above plain, price ............$1.50 Postage, 5c

**No. 316**—Frazier's spring shoulder holster; price ............$3.50 Postage, 5c

R. T. Frazier's catalog #31 shows several "Mexican loop" Pistol holsters and four shoulder holsters. Their #315 "Spring Shoulder Holster" appears to be a near copy of the Furstnow holster. The era of the thong stitch was here and many of these later holsters show this feature.

R. T. Frazier's Money and Cartridge belt combination. A close-up of the cartouche and the "long style" California nickeled buckle. Classified as their #303 belt with 36 loops, 2½ inches wide.

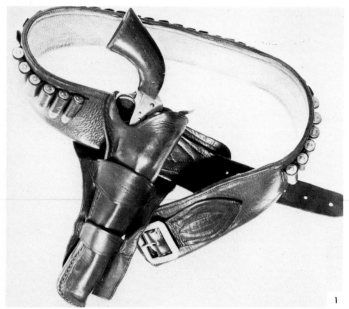
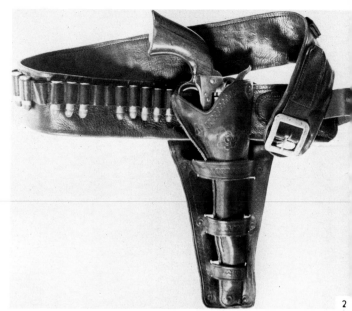

Still another R. T. Frazier Mexican style holster with two wide loops for a 7½″ Colt Single Action. The "Frazier" hallmark is stamped onto the upper holster loop as well as the buckle billet of the money belt. Note the extra width of the skirt as well as its short length.

A three looped Mexican style holster for a 7½″ Colt Single Action by R. T. Frazier probably represents a very early style as the pouch clearly resembles an old percussion "California Style" holster. The lower loop shows the Frazier cartouche. Note the squared-off skirt bottom.

| No. 409—Left Hand | No. 410—Left Hand | |
|---|---|---|
| Large | Medium | Small |
| For Revolvers | For Revolvers | For Revolvers |
| With 5½ to 7½″ barrels | With 4 to 5″ barrels | Under 4″ barrels |

### Left Hand Knapp Holsters

See description on page 9.
**We use these left hand cuts to call Special Attention to the fact that all Holsters in this catalogue can be supplied in either right or left hand at the same price.**

| | Large | Medium | Small |
|---|---|---|---|
| No. 409—Fine plain smooth finish | $3.25 | $3.00 | $2.75 |
| No. 509—Hand basket stamped | $4.00 | $3.50 | $3.25 |
| No. 709—Full Mexican hand carved | $4.75 | $4.25 | $3.50 |

No. 909—Made of medium weight leather, otherwise same as above.

| | Large | Medium | Small |
|---|---|---|---|
| No. 909—Fine plain smooth finish only | $3.00 | $2.75 | $2.50 |

### Quick Draw Holsters, Left Hand

Best quality, same as No. 409, but made with leather cut away to expose trigger.

| | Large | Medium | Small |
|---|---|---|---|
| No. 410—Fine plain smooth finish | $3.25 | $3.00 | $2.75 |
| No. 510—Hand basket stamped | $4.00 | $3.50 | $3.25 |
| No. 710—Full Mexican hand carved | $4.75 | $4.25 | $3.50 |

No. 910—Made of medium weight leather, otherwise same as No. 410.

| | Large | Medium | Small |
|---|---|---|---|
| No. 910—Fine plain smooth finish only | $3.00 | $2.75 | $2.50 |

The hostlers listed on this page are **not** made for automatics.

| No. 711—Large | No. 511—Medium | No. 411—Small |
|---|---|---|
| For Revolvers | For Revolvers | For Revolvers |
| With 5½ to 7½″ barrels | With 4 to 5″ barrels | Under 4″ barrels |

### Frontier Pattern Belt Holster

We have been making this old reliable pattern of holster longer than any other and is seems to be preferred by those who desire "The Box Fit."

Made of Extra Heavy Oak Tanned California skirting leather of one solid piece, waxed thread sewed, not lined, finest finish, very durable, closed end.

| | Large | Medium | Small |
|---|---|---|---|
| No. 411—Fine plain smooth finish | $3.25 | $3.00 | $2.75 |
| No. 511—Hand basket stamped | $4.25 | $3.75 | $3.25 |
| No. 711—Mexican hand carved | $4.75 | $4.25 | $3.75 |

No. 911—Made of medium weight leather, otherwise same as above.

| | Large | Medium | Small |
|---|---|---|---|
| No. 911—Fine plain smooth finish only | $3.00 | $2.75 | $2.50 |

Holsters of this pattern are **not** made for automatics.

A page from a Heiser catalog of 1928 showing several of the "Mexican loop" holsters being offered. Much valuable information can be gathered by a study of these old catalogs.

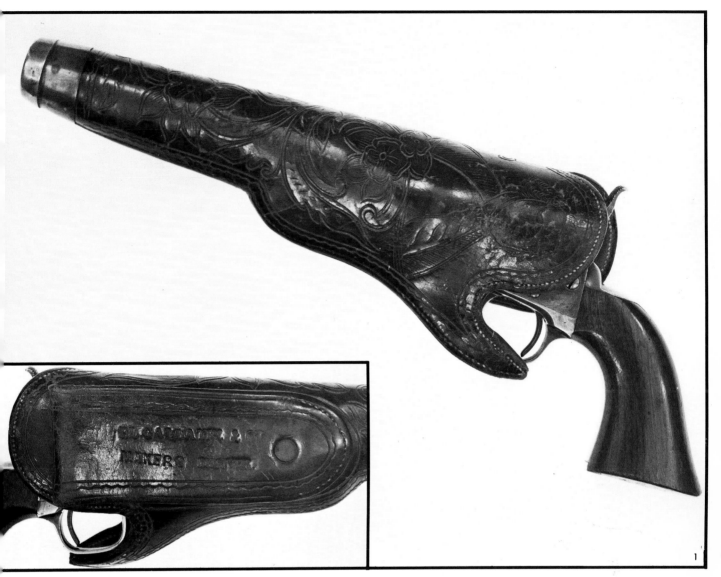

E. L. Gallatin & Co. of Denver made the early "California Style" slim-jim holsters for the Percussion revolvers of that day. Photo shows a rare example of this style holster. Note the typical double "S" curved top pouch contour and the simple hand cut design and bust of George Washington. The silver muzzle cap also afforded a measure of protection.

The back side of the E. L. Gallatin holster showing the primitive hallmark and simple copper riveted belt loop. Copper rivets, a carryover from the military, were used to a greater degree on the earlier holsters then on the later "Mexican loop" varieties. Note that the back of this holster is also tooled with a foliage pattern.

Greyhound Specialty Co. of Denver was probably a distributor or a retail outlet in that area. This holster fits a 3½″ Sheriff's model Colt and was probably manufactured for Greyhound Specialty Co., by H. H. Heiser. Nicely executed with a Mexican-style floral design.

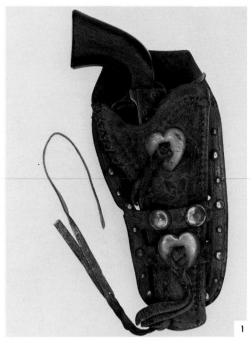

1

A well worn brass studded Single Action holster made by "Chas. Swope" of Montrose, Colo. The heart-shaped nickel plated brass top concho covers the maker's hallmark. Both conchos were probably added by a former owner. Well tooled with tiny characteristic "Rosettes" at all border design junctions. Mexican Style with two integral loops.

2

Heiser's #711 "Mexican Hand Carved" holster made of "extra heavy oak tanned California Skirting leather". Thong stitched, skirt not tooled. Maker's cartouche located on the skirt under the muzzle of the pouch. A semi-modern design with a matching hand tooled belt.

3

Heiser's #409 holster was supplied in either right or left hand versions at the same price. A rugged Mexican style, practical in all respects, made of an extra heavy saddle leather, has no "S" curve top pouch contour, and the muzzle remains open. The main seam has the "3-H" embossed rivet at the top.

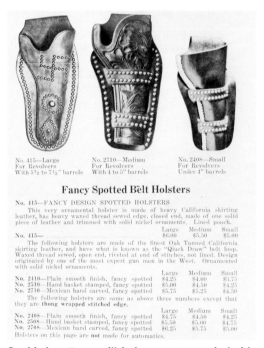

No. 415—Large
For Revolvers
With 5½ to 7½" barrels

No. 2710—Medium
For Revolvers
With 4 to 5" barrels

No. 2408—Small
For Revolvers
Under 4" barrels

**Fancy Spotted Belt Holsters**

No. 415—FANCY DESIGN SPOTTED HOLSTERS
This very ornamental holster is made of heavy California skirting leather, has heavy waxed thread sewed edge, closed end, made of one solid piece of leather and trimmed with solid nickel ornaments. Lined pouch.

| | Large | Medium | Small |
|---|---|---|---|
| No. 415— | $6.00 | $5.50 | $5.00 |

The following holsters are made of the finest Oak Tanned California skirting leather, and have what is known as the "Quick Draw" belt loop. Waxed thread sewed, open end, riveted at end of stitches, not lined. Design originated by one of the most expert gun men in the West. Ornamented with solid nickel ornaments.

| | Large | Medium | Small |
|---|---|---|---|
| No. 2110—Plain smooth finish, fancy spotted | $4.25 | $4.00 | $3.75 |
| No. 2510—Hand basket stamped, fancy spotted | $5.00 | $4.50 | $4.25 |
| No. 2710—Mexican hand carved, fancy spotted | $5.75 | $5.25 | $4.50 |

The following holsters are same as above three numbers except that they are thong wrapped stitched edge.

| | Large | Medium | Small |
|---|---|---|---|
| No. 2408—Plain smooth finish, fancy spotted | $4.75 | $4.50 | $4.25 |
| No. 2508—Hand basket stamped, fancy spotted | $5.50 | $5.00 | $4.75 |
| No. 2708—Mexican hand carved, fancy spotted | $6.25 | $5.75 | $5.00 |

Holsters on this page are **not** made for automatics.

Studded or "spotted" holsters are very desirable collector items. Though probably intended for parade use, a well worn, old studded holster really adds "color" to a Western holster collection.

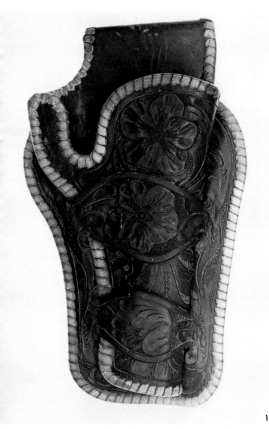

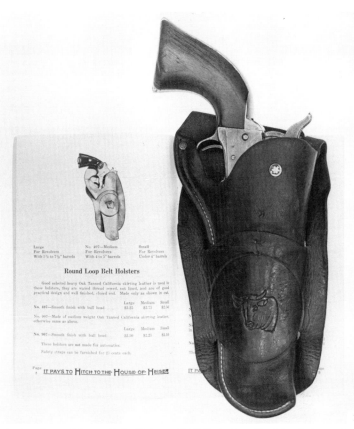

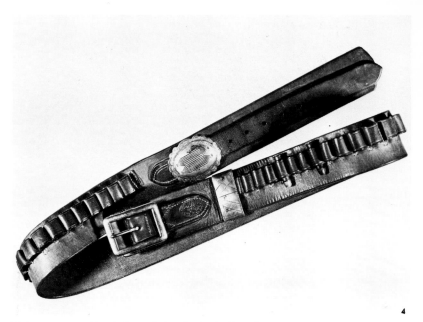

ictured on the cover of Heiser's Catalog #23, their
#753, "Extra Fine Belt Holster" features a leather lined
ouch and back, hand thong stitched with white lacing.
ell loop has two snap buttons for easy removal. Espe-
ially adapted for belts with extended loops. "Full Mexi-
an carved". A "Buscadero" holster. Semi-Modern.

Heiser's "Round Loop Belt Holster #907"; is described in their catalog
#20 of 1928 as "Smooth finish with bull head". Someone has added a
snap, and a strap which is now gone. The top rivet has the "3-H" logo and
the maker's cartouche is an oval located on the skirt under the muzzle area.
Shown with its original advertisement.

Heiser's #727 pattern "Original Laced Loop Belt Hol-
ter" Mexican hand carved, studding was probably
dded by a former owner, as it is not shown in the cata-
g. Note the elimination of the skirt, which would tend
 classify this holster out of the Mexican-loop classifi-
ation. The "leg thong" would indicate a former owner
as a "movie goer".

This super cartridge belt made by Fred Mueller of Denver measures 4 ft. 9 inches
long! It has 55 cartridge loops. It sports the "long pattern" California style belt
buckle and a silver concho and belt loop for decoration. The Fred Mueller cartouche is clearly seen on the buckle billet.

These beautiful saddle bags with an integral holster were manufactured in Marysville, Calif. by Victor Earnshields. They are marked "Wells Fargo & Co." and are considered to be one of the rarest forms of revolver conveyance. A product of California's mother-lode country, they were probably manufactured during the 1880's.

# California Makers

Many of the earliest saddle shops and holsters were located in California, beginning at the outset of the Gold Rush and continuing on through the 1900's. The "California Style" holster predominated during the percussion or Gold Rush days, and many interesting attractive holsters are to be found reflecting this wild frontier era. It is here where we see several "Sea Coast" saddlers recorded as well as the "Mother Lode" being represented by a maker from Marysville.

**Arana Saddlery,** San Luis Obispo, Cal., pre 1882.

**W. Davis & Son,** San Francisco, Cal., bought out by Keyston Brothers.

**E.T. Allen Co.,** San Francisco, Cal. manufactured a metal clip holster which fastens over the loading gate of a Colt Single Action to hold the revolver in position. "Dog Head" trademark.

**Victor Earnshields,** Marysville, Cal. Manufacturers, circa 1880

**S.H. Frank & Co.,** 410 Battery St., San Francisco, Cal. Suppliers of quality "Oakwood Leathers" to the Saddle making industry. The famous "Oak tanned California Skirting leathers" which were used to make holsters throughout the West probably originated at this tannery.

**G.S. Garcia,** Salinas, Cal., circa 1882, same as Garcia Saddlery of Elko, Nevada.

**J.C. Johnson Saddlery,** San Francisco, Cal. was purchased by the Keyston Bros.

**Keyston Bros.,** San Francisco, Cal.; The largest West Coast Saddlery. They were associated with Main & Winchester in 1867. Samuel Keyston retired in 1877, his sons James and William took over the business. They bought out J.C. Johnson and in 1912 bought out the L.D. Stone Co., who were the successors to Main & Winchester. In 1954 Keyston merged with the H.H. Heiser Co.

**Lichtenberger & Fergerson,** Los Angeles, Cal., Circa 1910.

**S. Loomis,** Santa Barbara, Cal.

**Main & Winchester,** San Francisco, Cal. Established in 1849. Going back to the Gold Rush days, this firm is without doubt the most famous California saddler. Surely their earliest products and especially their holsters helped to "set the pace" of those early days. They were located at No's 214-220 Battery Street. Their holsters exemplified the now standard "California Style" holsters so famous and desired by today's collector. Most of their earliest holsters were the "left-handed", butt forward types, a characteristic of the mode of that day.

**Visalia Saddlery,** Visalia, Cal. Began in 1863 by Juan Martarel. The business was purchased in 1870 by Henry Shuham and David Walker who received their earlier training and experience from Main & Winchester. Partnership dissolved in 1877 and Walker opened his own shop in Visalia in 1877. Edmond Weeks, Walker's nephew took over the Visalia Saddlery in 1899 and re-located to San Francisco until the 1906 earthquake. Weeks died in 1931 and the business was turned over to Leland Bergen. In 1959 the business was sold to Kenneth Copock, a Canadian.

**Wal-Rig,** Sacramento, Cal.

**B.T. Weitten,** Compton, Cal; a cartouche noted on an old cartridge belt.

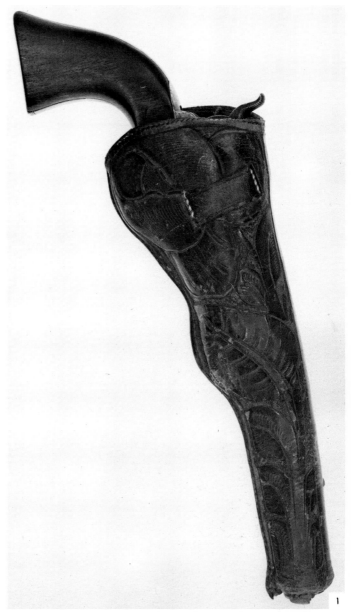

S. Loomis, Santa Barbara, Calif., made this California-Style deeply carved holster for a small-guard M1851 Colt Navy revolver. Original flap has been cut off. Old California made and "signed" California-style holsters are extremely sought after.

The Main & Winchester hallmark as found on the back-side of an early California-Style M1851 Navy holster. Also note the characteristic small belt loop usually attached with copper rivets.

Still another early "California-Style" carved holster. It is important to note the early style of these leather carving designs. They are seldom encountered on the "Mexican loop" holsters and seem to always be found in conjunction with these "California" or "slim-jim" holsters. This holster is estimated to be circa 1863 manufacture.

Though unsigned, this holster clearly illustrates a "transitional" type showing a "California style" pouch in combination with a "Mexican loop" style skirt and loop configuration. The typical "rosette" design at the top of the pouch is indicative of its early origin. Holsters which display these combination features are especially appreciated by collectors.

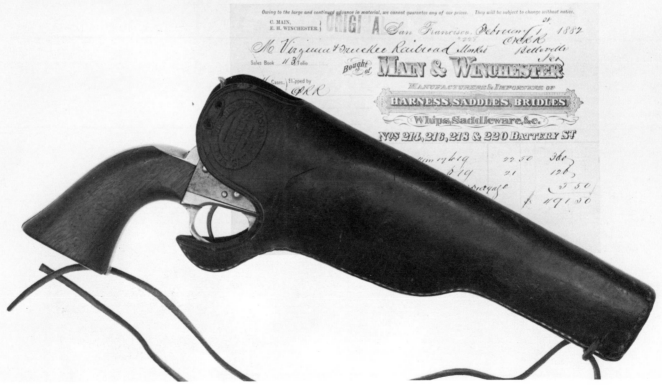

A very practical Main & Winchester contoured "California style" holster for a Colt Navy revolver. This too is a scarce variant, as generally these holsters are somewhat fancier. An original "Main & Winchester" billing is shown in the background.

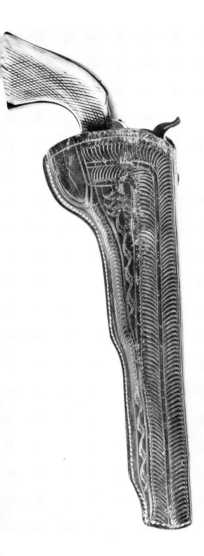

One of the most unique and rare examples of a Colt Dragoon, early California-style, hand tooled, civilian holster is represented by this Main & Winchester example. There is no question that this holster exemplifies the California Gold Rush days and has a significant historical association.

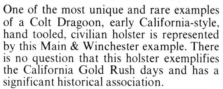

A "California style" holster formed to fit a M1851 Colt Navy, this holster sports an extremely straight leading edge, a wide "fern frond" design follows this edge and the upper pouch contour. This holster though "unsigned" departs from the typical "S" curve upper pouch contour, but the trigger guard area remains without design, so that at some later date this portion could have been removed without damaging or cutting into the tooled design.

A very early unsigned "California style" holster which fits a 7½" Colt Single Action. Note the pouch silhouette, which unlike its percussion counterparts does not contour around the percussion barrel lug. This is an extremely rare holster as it is out of context with the "Mexican loop" holsters then being manufactured for the Single Action Colt. A muzzle plug is fitted. Also note the unique hand-cut designs.

Main & Winchester's saddle bag and holster combination represent a truly unique and especially rare early California set. The "half-pouch" style integral holster is fitted with a Colt Pocket Navy revolver.

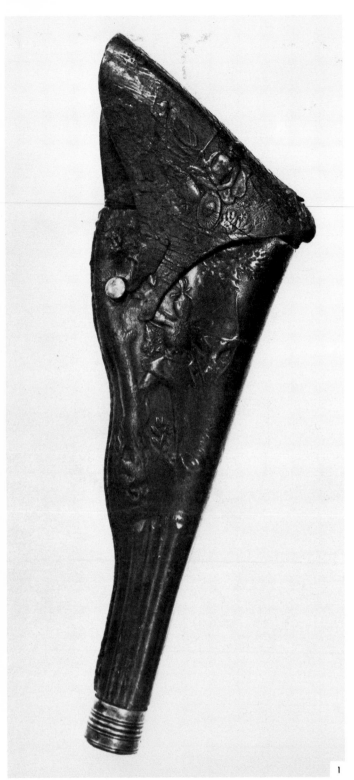

## Montana Makers

Miles City, Montana was located in the path of the Texas Trail and became the horse capitol of the world. Consequently, several major saddle shops were located there and some of the fine saddles produced there like the Coggshall's and Furstnow, were world renowned. Holsters too were of the best quality and are today considered prime collectables especially if manufactured during the "Territory" days.

**M.S. Bogwers Saddle Co.,** Miles City, Mont.

**C.E. Coggshall Saddle Co.,** Miles City, Mont. Coggshall worked in Furstnow's shop and later purchased the Moran business.

**W.B. Ten Eyck,** Billings, Mont. Billings was called Coulson until 1882, and Montana became a state in 1889. So this maker had to have worked circa 1882 through 1889.

**Al Furstnow,** Miles City, Mont. Began in 1884, one of the best known early saddlers and originator of the "Miles City Saddle". They featured a full line of saddles, saddle trees, Stirrips, Tapaderos, cinches, Chaparejos, Collars, and Cuffs, Headstalls, Quirts, belts and holsters. Their "Sheriffs Lightening Spring Shoulder Holster" is well known among collectors. Their spurs were listed as being among the finest available.

**E. Goettlich,** Miles City, Mont., circa 1880's. Al Furstnow worked for Goettlich in 1884.

**Miles City Saddlery Co.,** Miles City, Mont. This famous saddlery was officially begun in 1909 by a partnership of Frank Jelinek, Bert Coleman and Clem Kathmann who bought out Coggshall. Coggshall remained as a "silent" Vice President and his name was used to continue the production of the famous "Cogshall Saddle".

**Hugh Moran,** Miles City, Montana Territory. Probably the first saddlery in Miles City. Remained in business until bought out by Coggshall circa 1875.

**Chas. Racek,** Billings, Mont. Territory, 1883-1889.

**Robbins & Lenoier,** Miles City, Mont. Territory, circa 1881.

**Jos. Sullivan & Co.,** Ft. Benton, Montana Territory.

**Wm. Wellman,** White Sulpher Springs, Mont. Wellman was born in 1844 and died in 1929.

This example truly represents the epitome of an early California Gold Rush holster. The modified "full flap" and square top pouch contour are reminiscent of the then current military holsters, but this is a right-handed holster, quite a departure from the norm of those days. The holster accepts a Colt M1851 square-backed Navy revolver, is fluted at the muzzle end with a brass end cap. The holster is decorated in relief with a Mohawk Indian with drawn bow in a forest scene. The flap is decorated by the California state seal, showing a gold miner, pick and shaker with a "side-wheeler" ship in the background.

William Wellman of White Sulpher Springs, Montana made this interesting "Mexican loop" variant with a "riveted loop". Nicely tooled and marked with the maker's cartouche on the wide loop.

Jos. Sullivan & Co., Ft. Benton, M.T.; a matching belt and left-handed holster rig was manufactured before Montana became a State on November 8, 1889. A very interesting short skirted "Mexican style" holster showing almost a "California" or "slim-jim" pouch profile. Maker's cartouche is prominently stamped on the upper pouch.

1

A Moran Bros. Miles City, MT holster for a Colt Single Action, features a short skirt, a single wide "riveted loop" and an interesting "S" curved top pouch contour. Holster is buckskin lined.

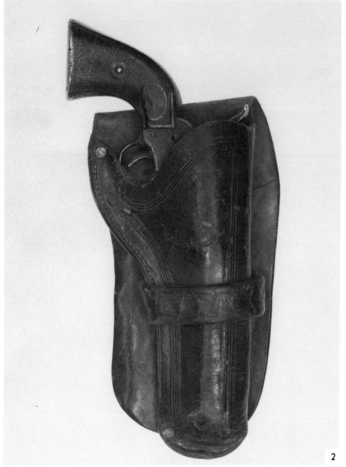

2

A Miles City Saddlery Co. holster, Mexican style with "riveted loop", made for a 4¾″ Colt Single Action. Simple line border on the pouch with the typical "rosettes" at the junctions. Main seam is reinforced at the top and bottom with an iron rivet. A rather scarce holster.

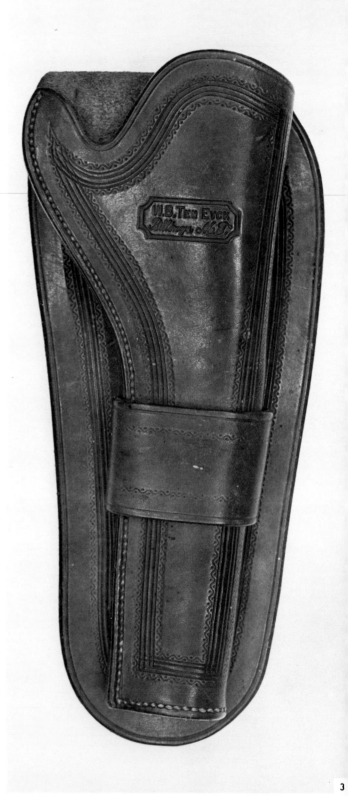

3

Without doubt this excellent Montana Territory holster made by "W. B. Ten Eyck" of Billings, remains today as a prime example of an early pre-1889 manufactured holster in new condition. This holster fits a M1851 Colt Navy revolver and features a "Cheyenne plug", a characteristic of the northern cattle country. It is interesting that though the Colt Single Action was in full production during the time of this holster's manufacture, it was made instead for the old percussion Colt Navy revolver. Generally we find that the "riveted loop" holsters, as in this example were not made for percussion revolvers. The survival of this holster in new unused condition may be partly attributed to the fact that it was made for a then obsolete revolver.

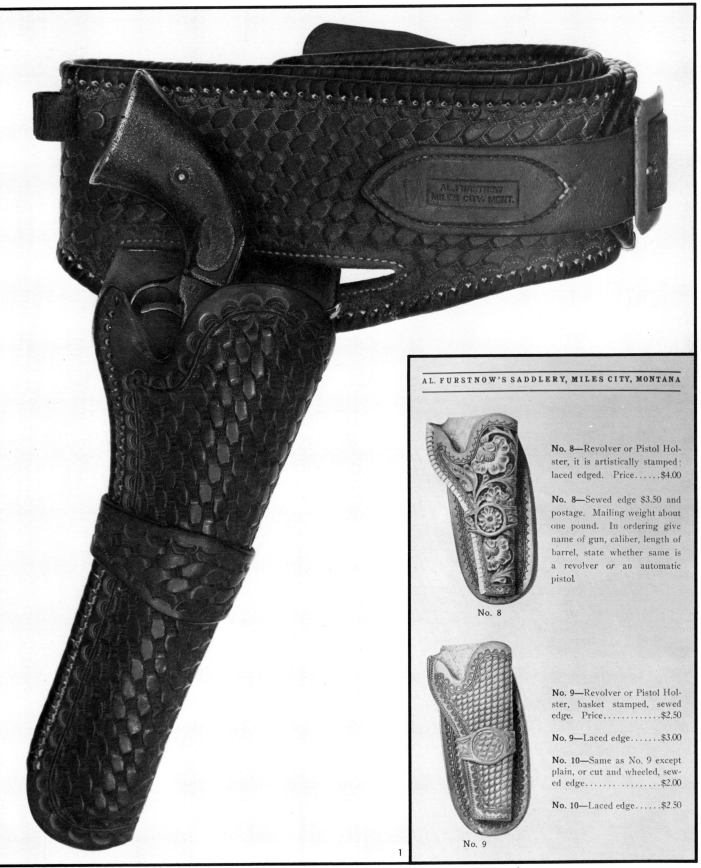

AL. FURSTNOW'S SADDLERY, MILES CITY, MONTANA

**No. 8**—Revolver or Pistol Holster, it is artistically stamped; laced edged. Price......$4.00

**No. 8**—Sewed edge $3.50 and postage. Mailing weight about one pound. In ordering give name of gun, caliber, length of barrel, state whether same is a revolver or an automatic pistol.

No. 8

**No. 9**—Revolver or Pistol Holster, basket stamped, sewed edge. Price............$2.50

**No. 9**—Laced edge.......$3.00

**No. 10**—Same as No. 9 except plain, or cut and wheeled, sewed edge.................$2.00

**No. 10**—Laced edge......$2.50

No. 9

ndicative of the movie influence is this Furstnow "Buscadero rig". The basket weave, 7½″ Colt S.A. holster hangs from its matching "looped" belt. The skirt of the holster has been eliminated and we begin to see the end of the era of the "Mexican loop" holster. Circa 920's.

A page from Al Furstnow's catalog; possibly from the 1930's since the basket weave and thong lacing features, now considered semi-modern, are apparent. None the less, the real quality of these nice collectable holsters is evident.

# Utah Makers

Several saddlers were found throughout "Mormon Country" and though they were first to admit to a non-violent society a few holsters must have been manufactured to help "keep the peace".

**Bee Saddlery,** Provo, Utah, still in business.
**Browning Bros.,** Ogden, Utah, Closed in 1926.
**Burns Saddlery,** Salina, Utah, Territory.
**Cornish & Walton Saddlers,** Ogden, Utah, Circa 1892.
**Durrant Bros.,** Circa 1870's to 1900.
**Hodgman Saddlery,** Ogden, Utah, circa 1889, was bought out by J.C. Read & Bros.
**J.W. Jenkins,** Salt Lake City, Utah, Circa 1875-1970.
**Newton Bros.,** Vernal, Utah.
**J.C. Read & Bros.,** Ogden, Utah. Successor to Hodgman Co.

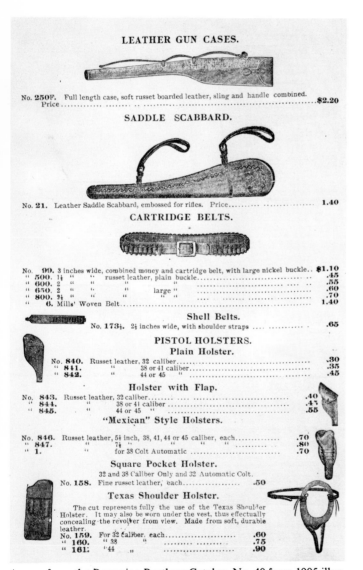

This "Mexican loop" Safety Strap Belt Holster was made for Browning Brothers of Ogden, Utah by H. H. Heiser. It is thong wrapped and made of "extra heavy" saddle leather. The main-seam top rivet has the distinctive "3-H" logo which positively identifies this holster as being made by Heiser.

A page from the Browning Brothers Catalog, No. 40 from 1905 illustrates several varieties of holsters and cartridge belts. It is clearly borne out in this catalog that the holsters with loops in their skirts were referred to as "Mexican" style.

A close-up of the Browning Bros. logo.

# Missouri Makers

St. Louis was of course an "outfitting" town for the early migrants before the Railroad, so it and the other Missouri towns were fitting places in which to find old saddlery shops. We have listed but a few of these Missouri Saddlers.

**Paul Askew** (1866) or **Askew Bros.** (1890), Kansas City, lasted until 1910.

**Bauer Bros.,** St. Louis, Mo. "Moose Brand" holsters considered as a semi-modern maker.

**Charles Shipley,** Kansas City, Mo. began in 1885 spanned three generations until 1967. Were located at 1527-31 Genesee Street in Kansas City.

**Sickles Saddlery,** St. Louis, Established in 1834.

**Wyeth Hardware Mfg. Co.,** St. Joseph, Mo.

Established 1885.  Catalogue No. 12  Incorporated 1910.

Main Offices and Factory
Opposite Live Stock Exchange Building.

From Factory to Consumer Direct.

From Factory to Consumer Direct

Write us for any information about Leather Goods . . . . . . .

## Chas. P. Shipley Saddlery and Mercantile Co.

*Wholesale and Retail Manufacturers of*

### Harness and Saddles, Boots and Shoes and All Kinds of Leather Goods

1527, 1529, 1531 Genesee Street,  Kansas City, Mo.

The title page from a Chas. P. Shipley catalog (1912) illustrates the size of this concern. Though many saddlers were quite large, many manufactured only a few holster styles. Four of the Shipley holsters are shown at the top of this photo.

2

A two looped semi-modern Single Action holster for a 7½″ Colt manufactured by Bauer Bros., Inc. St. Louis. The lower skirt shows a moose head logo and is labeled "Moose Brand Sporting Goods". Modern characteristics include; a machine embossed pouch and angular thong stitching. Interestingly, it retains the "rosette" design on the upper band reminiscent of the older frontier-style holsters. Holster and badge belonged to a Montana Sheriff.

A Bauer Brothers "Moose Brand" holster, made in St. Louis, Mo. Characteristic "Mexican loop" style; simple line embossed border design. This holster though semi-modern still sports the "Mexican" two loop design, showing the distinctive "Moosehead" logo on the upper modified loop. It fits a 4¾″ Colt Single Action revolver.

# Arizona Makers

There can be no doubt in the collectors mind that Arizona represents one of the most historical Western areas of our Frontier. The Great Indian Wars with the Chiricahuas and Apaches; the several U.S. Army Forts; the mining towns of Tombstone & Bisbe; the Copper Queen Mine, John P. Clum; the Erps, John C. Freemont, Buffalo Bill; and the story goes on and on. Arizona collectables from the Frontier days therefore represent a great historical heritage, and the saddle makers of those days helped to perpetuate this influence.

**Arizona Saddlery Co.,** Prescott, Arizona; Listed in the 1922 City Directory as being owned by a Frank Olzer and located at 139 N. Cortez St. In 1931 the City Directory lists this concern as being owned by a R.L. Cunningham and their address was 136 N. Cortez. No further listing was shown in the 1935 or 1936 directories.

**J.S. Calles,** Prescott, Ariz. Territory.

**Chase E. Collins,** Globe, Ariz.

**N. Porter** (Porter Bros.), Phoenix, Ariz. Begun in Tyler, Texas, business destroyed by fire. In 1885 business was again started in Abilene, Texas and later moved to Phoenix, Ariz. Earl H. Porter (1879-1925) controlled the business for nineteen years.

**F.J. Villaescusa,** Tucson, Arizona Territory.

This young Arizona gentleman sports a fine fringed holster with an unidentified square-backed trigger guard revolver. The photo is autographed "James W. Scott", the photographer was J. C. Burge of Flagstaff, AZ.

Arizona Saddlery Co., Prescott, Arizona. A neat old Arizona holster simple in design with a single wide loop showing the maker's hall mark deeply branded into the leather. Holster now fits a 4¾″ Colt Single Action, but was cut down from a longer length.

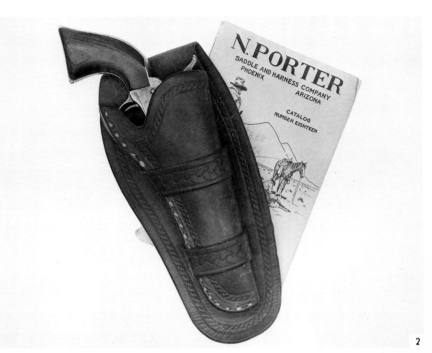

Mexican-style single looped holster made by
. J. Villaescusa, Tucson, A.T. Another nice
rritorial holster which undoubtedly saw some
xciting days. This holster's loop appears to be
later modification or repair. Nicely hand
oled in the Mexican style.

A very nicely made "N. Porter" Mexican style double riveted looped holster was identified by a picture located in their 1931 catalog. It is described as follows: "Holster for
Colts or S&W Frontier Six Shooter. Border reeled as shown. Price, $2.00." The impor-
tance of old catalogs is illustrated, as this unmarked example would never have been
identified unless its advertisement had been found.

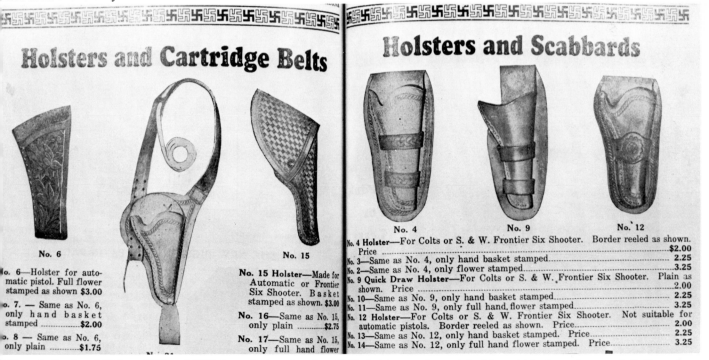

## Holsters and Cartridge Belts

**No. 6**

o. 6—Holster for auto-
matic pistol. Full flower
stamped as shown $3.00

o. 7. — Same as No. 6,
only hand basket
stamped ..............$2.00

o. 8 — Same as No. 6,
only plain ..........$1.75

**No. 15**

No. 15 Holster—Made for
Automatic or Frontier
Six Shooter. Basket
stamped as shown. $3.00

No. 16—Same as No. 15,
only plain ...........$2.75

No. 17—Same as No. 15,
only full hand flower

## Holsters and Scabbards

**No. 4**      **No. 9**      **No. 12**

No. 4 Holster—For Colts or S. & W. Frontier Six Shooter. Border reeled as shown.
Price ...................................................................................$2.00
No. 3—Same as No. 4, only hand basket stamped...................................2.25
No. 2—Same as No. 4, only flower stamped...........................................3.25
No. 9 Quick Draw Holster—For Colts or S. & W. Frontier Six Shooter. Plain as
shown. Price ...........................................................................2.00
No. 10—Same as No. 9, only hand basket stamped...................................2.25
No. 11—Same as No. 9, only full hand. flower stamped..............................3.25
No. 12 Holster—For Colts or S. & W. Frontier Six Shooter. Not suitable for
automatic pistols. Border reeled as shown. Price..................................2.00
No. 13—Same as No. 12, only hand basket stamped. Price.........................2.25
No. 14—Same as No. 12, only full hand flower stamped. Price.....................3.25

. Porter's Catalog # 18 from 1930 and 1931 shows their series of available holsters, and a neat double cartridge looped money belt. It was from
is page that we were able to identify the foregoing illustration's unmarked holsters.

43

This fine matching J. S. Collins & Co., Cheyenne, Wyo., rig shows a rather rare Collins "Mexican loop" holster with two riveted loops, and a very narrow skirt. This holster was probably originally fitted with a "Cheyenne" muzzle plug but it's now "long gone".

# Wyoming Saddlers

Wyoming became a state on July 10, 1890, it is therefore quite possible to acquire holsters and other leather goods which were made during its territorial days. Because of Wyoming's cattle and mining industries a need was there for saddlers. Several saddlers settled in the area and began to produce top quality leather goods. The names "Meanea" or "Gallatin" are of course well known old-time Wyoming makers and their holsters always seem to demand a premium from collectors.

**J.S. Collins,** Cheyenne, Wyo. Territory, went into business with his brother George H. Collins. Later moved to Omaha where another partner was added, and this shop was called Collins & Morrison. This shop ran until 1896, when it was sold to "A. Cornish". Other Collins shops were located in Billings and Great Falls.

**E.L. Gallatin & Co.,** Cheyenne, Wyo. Territory. A great Wyoming territorial maker.

**Eldred & Morrow,** Sheridan, Wyo.

**L.H. Hatch,** Pinedale, Wyo., marked "K-O" for K-BAR-O Ranch. Circa 1930's.

**Frank Meanea,** Cheyenne, Wyo. Frank Meanea Gallatin's nephew purchased this shop in 1873. Meanea was born in 1849 near Lexington, Missouri; in 1867 he moved to Nebraska City. In 1868 he moved to Bear River City. Later he opened the Gallatin shop as manager for his uncle. He purchased this shop in 1876, moved to another location in 1927 and died in November, 1928 in Golden, Colo. Meanea holsters are today rated as extremely desirable collector items.

**R.S. Pane,** Pinedale, Wyo.

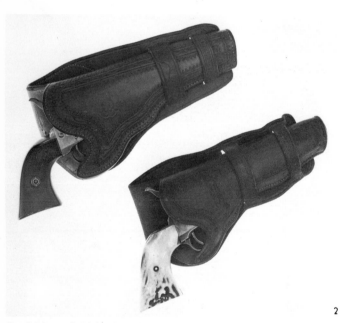

Frank Meanea's "deluxe" model holster is illustrated in the upper figure. It is listed as "No. 1 Border Stamp, buckskin lined, $5.00." Both holsters feature the "Cheyenne plug" a characteristic which probably originated with Frank Meanea's Uncle E. L. Gallatin. Both holsters are almost exact duplicates of the Gallatin design. The lower illustrated holster is listed as: "No. 2, Plain, Not stamped, or lined, $3.50", though a fine lined border stamping is evident. These holsters are described in Frank Meanea's own words: "Above are my own make, hand sewn with gusset for triggerguard. When ordering state make and caliber of pistol, length of barrel and action, single or double."

This unbelievable Meanea "rig" represents one of the finest we've encountered. A 7½" Colt, "fishscale" design holster, "Mexican loop" style, with one super wide loop and an extra wide plain skirt. The Meanea marked money belt with a double row of 45 Colt cartridges is also a prime collectable. Note the absence of the "Cheyenne Plug" in this holster.

Though "unsigned", this well made double looped money belt illustrates a slightly different style than the foregoing illustration. A close-up is shown so that the reader will be able to familiarize himself with the fine quality and workmanship of these old money belts. The iron, non-plated "California style" buckle lends interest to this fine belt.

A page from Frank Meanea's catalog showing the standard and deluxe holsters, a money belt, cuffs, etc. Holsters which were made by Meanea are very desirable collectors items today.

Made by L. H. Hatch, Pinedale, Wyoming, this unique holster represents two dramatic departures from the norm. The integral cartridge loops and leg-thong would indicate a custom made, semi-modern design. Lester H. Hatch was a bootmaker and leather craftsman in Pinedale during the early 1930's.

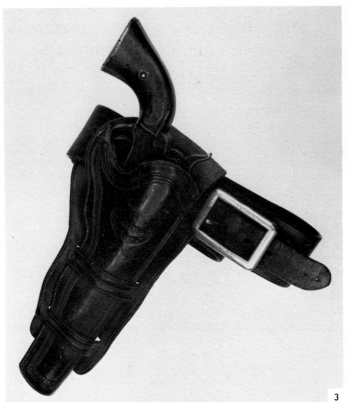

Eldred & Morrow, Cheyenne, Wyoming made this seldom encountered "Cheyenne" holster. Note the single wide loop, the "Cheyenne plug", and the "bullseye" design on the loop. All of these characteristics are pleasingly accented by the well executed border designs.

E. L. Gallatin & Co., Cheyenne, Wyo. Territory made this "Mexican loop" holster for a 7½″ Colt Single Action. The lines of this holster seem to characterize other Cheyenne makers products. Note the "swollen" portion of the pouch between the loops which helped to "lock in" the pouch. Fitted with the "Cheyenne plug" the design is almost a perfect match to the Meanea holster.

This photo which is simply labeled "A Cow Boy, New Mexico", illustrates well the style of "working gear" which was used by the cowboy of the old West. Note the neat double-looped Mexican holster, the cartridge belt, chaps and spurs.

## New Mexico Makers

Though we were not able to illustrate any of the New Mexico manufactured holsters, a limited amount of activity in this field did occur in New Mexico. We are listing three New Mexico makers from our files.

**E.T. Amonett,** Roswell, New Mexico. We were able to refer to this maker's catalog #37 (undated) and find that his business was located at 210 N. Main Street in Roswell. Many fine saddles, spurs, chaps and only four "Pistol Scabbards" are shown. The "Mexican Loop" holster illustrated in this catalog, shows a single loop which is hand carved, or "raised stamped" and "buck lined". A fine 4 inch cartridge belt is also shown and described as follows; "4 inch wide, made of the best grade of Pebble chap leather, buck hand stitched".
**John M. Hughes,** Albuquerque, New Mexico.
**Ed Seitzler & Co.,** Silver City, New Mexico.

This cabinet photo of "Juan, Chief Scout" from Fort Wingate, New Mexico shows this Indian with a double wide looped "Mexican loop" holster and two cartridge belts with California style buckles. In his hands he holds the muzzle of a Springfield M1873 Carbine. The saddle ring and bar have been removed as was the Indian practice of that day.

# Kansas Manufacturers

When one thinks of Kansas in light of Western history, the towns of Dodge City and Coffeyville immediately come to mind. Much history was written in these old colorful towns and leather goods from these days are treasured by collectors today. Only six Kansas "makers" are represented in our survey of this area, and more are surely to be found.

**Askew Brothers,** Kansas City, Kansas 1866-1910.
**H. Blickhahn & Co.,** Medicine Lodge, Kansas.
**G.S. Saddle So.,** Kansas City, Kansas.
**Hillmer Leather Shop,** Topeka, Kansas.
**L. Kipper & Sons,** Atchinson, Kansas.
**Standiford & Youmans & Co.,** Medicine Lodge, Kansas

These three "Dodge City Boys" are dressed in their gentleman's attire, each wearing his "sixgun" in a neat "Mexican loop" holster. Each man has an additional "backup" revolver or derringer stuck under his belt. The gentleman on the left sports a neat three-looped Mexican holster for a 7½″ Single Action Colt.

Made by "T. Price, Tulsa", Indian Territory, this 5½″ Colt Single Action holster departs from the usual "Mexican loop" design. It is a two piece holster with the "half pouch" sewn onto the skirt. A very unique design. A simple line border design outlines the pouch. The rivet at the muzzle end may be a later reinforcement.

A fine "Kansas rig" is represented by this illustration showing a Kansas made money belt by "T. Kipper & Sons, Atchinson, KS." and a nice 7½″ Colt Single Action holster made by "H. Blickhahn & Co." of "Medicine Lodge, KS". This holster features a double loop, contoured pouch, is buckskin lined, with a sewn-in "Cheyenne" muzzle plug, and a double stitched main seam. A simple "woven-line" rolled on design covers the pouch and loop areas.

# Oklahoma and Indian Territory

Oklahoma gained statehood on November 16, 1907. Prior to this date it was called Oklahoma or Indian Territory. So again we find that "territorial marked" holsters could be located from this area. We have but three "makers" listed for this state, two of which are territorial makers:

**L. Price,** Tulsa, Indian Territory
**D.L. Swent,** Hugo, Okla.
**A.E. Wilson,** Tulsa Indian Territory.

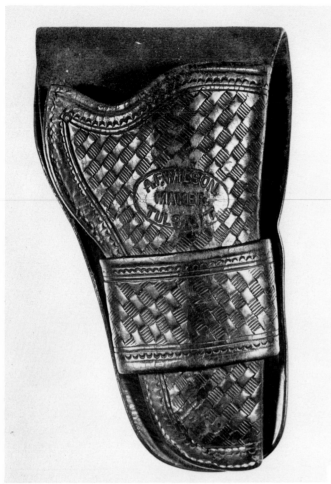

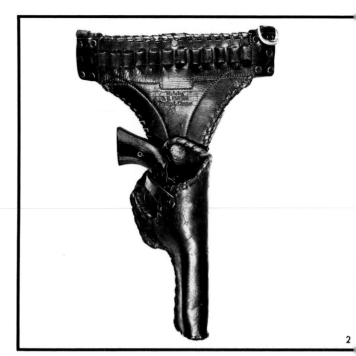

Though somewhat crude by comparison, this swivel holster departs from all recognized concepts of holster design! It was made by S. E. Emery, of Portland, Oregon, probably to fit a customer's particular needs. The low-slung swivel design was probably innovated to try to circumvent the rigidity of a leg-thonged "Buscadero" rig.

This extra short holster, which probably fits a Colt Sheriff's Model was made by, "A. F. Wilson, Tulsa, Indian Territory." Note the **early** use of what we refer to as "semi-modern" basket weave design. This riveted-loop holster also sports an extremely shallow "S" curve upper pouch contour.

## Nebraska Makers

Only two "makers" are listed in our survey as having worked in Nebraska.

**A. Cornish,** Omaha, Nebr. Purchased the Collins & Morrison shop, circa 1896.
**Fred Mantley,** Grand Rapids, Nebr., circa 1885.

## Oregon Saddle Shops

Oregon saddlers number but four in our current listing. Central and Eastern Oregon of course was cattle country and a "Round Up" was held in Pendleton.

**Farley & Frank,** The Dalles, Oregon. A semi-modern maker.
**S.E. Emery,** Portland, Oregon, Semi-modern.
**Hamley & Co.,** Pendleton, Ore., began in 1883 in Ashton, South Dakota, moved to Pendleton on June 5, 1905. First catalog published in 1909. Catalog No. 29 was dated 1929.
**George Lawrence & Co.,** Portland, Ore. Established circa 1857 by Samuel Sherlock. Purchased in 1874 and in 1893 was re-named the George Lawrence Co. They are noted for their fine holsters. Still in business.

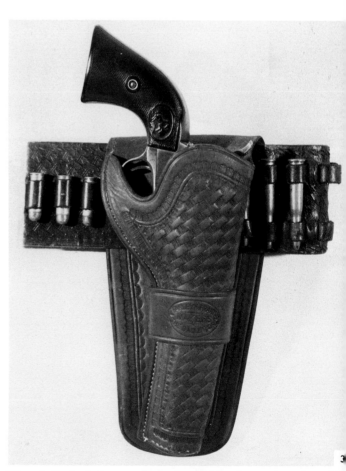

Though the basket weave design is considered a semi-modern characteristic in this study, we have included this Oregon maker: "Farley & Frank", of The Dalles, Oregon. A single loop Mexican style with "Cheyenne plug" closing the muzzle opening of the pouch.

# Nevada Saddlers

The great mining state of Nevada is represented in ur study by three Elko makers. Elko, Nevada, the seat f Nevada's cattle country was therefore the logical lo- ation for these three saddle shops. One of these shops, he Garcia Saddlery Co. is almost in a class by itself.

This famous company was named for and operated y G.S. Garcia. He was awarded first prize at the Chi- ago World's Fair for his famous $5,000.00 saddle, *hich was mounted with diamonds, gold and silver. He lso won first prize at the St. Louis World's Fair and the ewis & Clark Exposition. The "Mexican style" leather arving accomplished by this shop was the finest ever roduced. His fancy bits and spurs were silver inlayed nd possibly the finest ever produced. Garcia Rawhide attas are today prized for their workmanship. Though ieir catalog No. 28 for 1934 shows only two holsters, iese two are unique. One is nicely Mexican carved with flap. The tongue of the flap goes through a tight loop n the pouch; no skirt, nor loops. The other illustrated olster has no skirt, open top and is probably for a maller revolver. The name "Garcia" was synonymous *ith the best.

**J.M. Capriola Co., Elko, Nevada.** Joe Capriola Sr. founded this company in 1929. His experience was gained at the Gar- cia Saddlery. He was later assisted by his son Joe Jr. who passed away in 1947. The shop was then sold to Frank Jayo in 1955. In 1958 because of illness the shop was sold to Paul and Betty Bear. The J.M. Capriola Company still remains to- day, "better than ever".

**E.E. Meek, Maker, Elko, Nevada.** This cartouche has been observed on the illustrated holster.

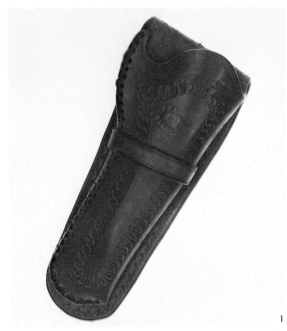

Though semi-modern in style, this "riveted loop" neatly made "E. E. Meek", Elko, Nevada holster is the only Nevada made holster we were able to illustrate. It was made for a 7½" Colt Single Action and sports a thong- stitched main-seam. It is made of extra heavy skirting, with simple hand-tooled border designs.

No. 185

**Pouch Shoulder Holster**

The pouch, back and shoulder strap of this pouch shoulder holster is made of oak tanned, medium weight russet leather. Shoulder strap has six cartridge loops and is laced on one side so that it can be adjusted to size wanted. The soft leather retaining strap is sewed on one side and is to be tied on other side through loop. Button hole tab at bottom is to be fastened to pants button to hold holster in position. In ordering state caliber of cartridge, name of gun and length of barrel.

N. 185—Plain finish only. To fit any gun. Each....................$2.50

This holster is made for those who do not care for the better grades.

Page 38 IT PAYS TO HITCH TO THE HOUSE OF HEISER

# Shoulder Holsters

Several of the old saddlery shops manufactured shoulder holsters. Al Furstnow of Miles City was well known for his "Sheriff's Lightning Spring Shoulder Hol- ster" which he espoused as "absolutely the fastest action holster on the market today".

In his excellent ARMS GAZETTE article, "Frontier Shoulder Holsters", Bill Mackin (April, 1978) classifies three distinct varieties of early shoulder holsters.

1. The "Texas Style" which was a simple sewn "half pouch" and skirt type and was probably the earliest type used by both lawmen and out- laws when concealment and speed began to be desirable traits.

2. The "Skeleton", a spring clip shoulder holster in which a raw-hide covered clip clasped the re- volver over its cylinder, while the muzzle of the revolver rested in a "boot" sewn onto the skirts' lower part. This is generally believed to be the style originated by Al Furstnow.

3. The "Half Breed", probably was a much later in- novation. This style of shoulder holster featured a spring-loaded pouch in which the area gener- ally sewn with a main-seam was left open and the revolver could be pulled forward and out with rapidity. This style holster is of course con- sidered the fore-runner of our modern day spring-loaded holsters.

All shoulder holsters had a rather wide shoulder strap and most had a narrower strip of leather or linen which was buckled around the chest to secure the "rig". Though quite cumbersome with 7½" Colt Single Ac- tions, these shoulder rigs have continued in popularity today and are used in conjunction with some of today's shorter "snub-nosed" revolvers.

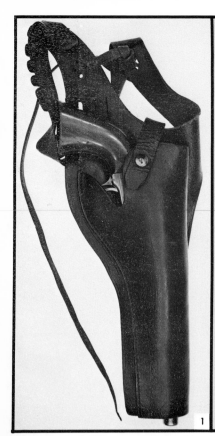  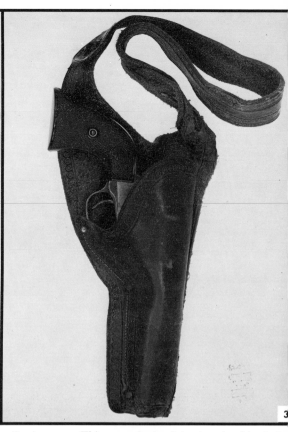

An unmarked "Texas style" shoulder holster, made with the pouch sewn onto the skirt. Light in weight, it shows a very faint delicate "vine" embossing on its border near the sewn edge. The japanned iron snap on the revolver's retaining strap helped to hold the Single Action securely in place. Extra cartridge loops are sewn onto the shoulder strap.

Furstnow's "Sheriffs' Lightning Spring Shoulder Holster. This is absolutely the fastest action holster on the market today. Furstnow's No. 3 answers every need in a fast action holster and is not bulky". So states the description of this famous holster in the Al Furstnow catalog No. 18. A very nice addition to any holster collection.

This unmarked soft leather shoulder holster is of the "Texas Style" and fits a 4¾" Colt Single Action nicely. It shows a circle-dot border design which borders the skirt, pouch and strap. A very early "shoulder rig" which exemplified the need for concealment in those early days.

Though unmarked, this neat shoulder rig shows early characteristics and markings. The rosette design on the pouch's central area and at the border junctions speak of its early (probably 1880's) beginning. The pouch is lined. Note the extra set of available cartridges found sewn in the loops on the strap.

# Mexican and Indian Holsters

Though the "Mexican Loop" has become a standard type of American holster, we do find that many finely made holsters of Mexican origin were manufactured and used in the old frontier days. The Mexican style and tooling is of course a very distinct and desirable feature carried over into some of the finest American made holsters. The Mexican influence, therefore, cannot be disputed when it comes to the frontier holster.

Besides the typically "Mexican style" loop holster there is a style of Mexican holster which is purely Mexican in design. These are the finely braided holsters and belts which came out of Mexico during these old days. Many are embellished with gold braiding, showing exquisite patterns. Some even sport the Mexican Eagle and Serpent motif. These beautiful Mexican holsters must be considered as top collector items and an art form which is probably lost today.

An Indian made frontier holster represents a pleasant departure from our usual line of thought when western holsters are contemplated. Though these are unique in their style and adornment, after all, they are as true a western holster as was ever made! Through the kindness of Mr. James O. Aplan we are fortunate to be able to illustrate and describe this rare Indian-made holster.

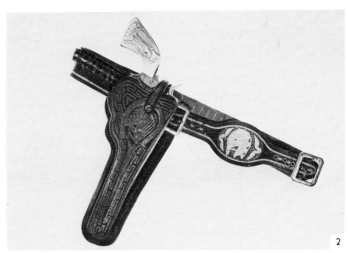

A truly magnificent gold braided Mexican made Single Action holster features a "loopless" construction. The horse-head, circled by a horse shoe design is braided into both the holster and the matching belt patterns. The Aztec influence seems to prevail in the holster's line design.

# Trade-Named Holsters

Trade named holsters are those early frontier holsters which were made for and sold by the larger, generally eastern, supply houses. Though most of these holsters are not marked by their makers, their patterns and styles may, in some cases, be traced to an individual well-known maker. These holsters are in most cases marked with a "logo" of intertwined letters representing the retail house by which they were sold. Many of these holsters are well made. They are quite collectable today as most of these "eastern houses" were also distributors of Colt, Smith & Wesson and other makes of revolvers. It is therefore quite possible today to have a Colt Single Action which was originally shipped to a certain "outlet" displayed with an original holster from that same retailer displaying his "logo".

**Abercrombie & Fitch,** New York.
**Hibbard, Spencer, Bartlett & Co.,** Chicago, "Ills" Featured a complete line of "Guns, Rifles, Ammunition, Revolvers, Fishing Tackle, and Sporting Goods". They were located at Lake Street and Wabash Ave.
**Merwin & Bray Co.,** Worchester, Mass and New York. A large Eastern house who, for a time, also manufactured firearms.
**Montgomery Ward,** Chicago, Ill.
**"Royal",** A trademark of an unknown distributor.
**Schyler, Hartley & Graham,** New York.
**Sears, Roebuck & Co.,** Chicago, Ill. Holsters were observed in several of their older catalogs.
**Shapleigh Hardware,** St. Louis, Mo. "Diamond Brand".
**Von Lengerke & Antoine,** Chicago, Ill. This company was bought out by Abercrombie & Fitch.

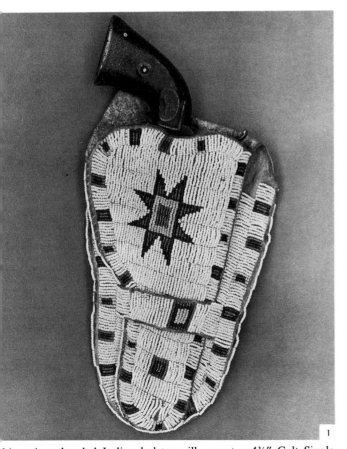

his unique beaded Indian holster will accept a 4¾" Colt Single ction. It came from the Rosebud Indian Reservation in South akota. Beaded holsters are quite rare. This example is beaded with ed-beads, sinew sewn on buckskin, and is backed with rawhide, to ive it more body. The designs are typically Sioux with geometric atterns.

This Abercrombie & Fitch Co.'s holster has the "A.F." logo in a circle on the lower skirt lip. A heavy tempered leather with the unique Heiser "Circle loop" formed from the skirt. Manufactured for distribution by Abercrombie & Fitch by Heiser of Denver, it is riveted at the top main seam with the famous "3-H" rivet. This holster fits a 7½″ Colt Single Action. A well pronounced "S" curve silhouette makes this a nice rig. A less elaborate holster of this same general pattern, but without the "3-H" iron rivet, has also been observed.

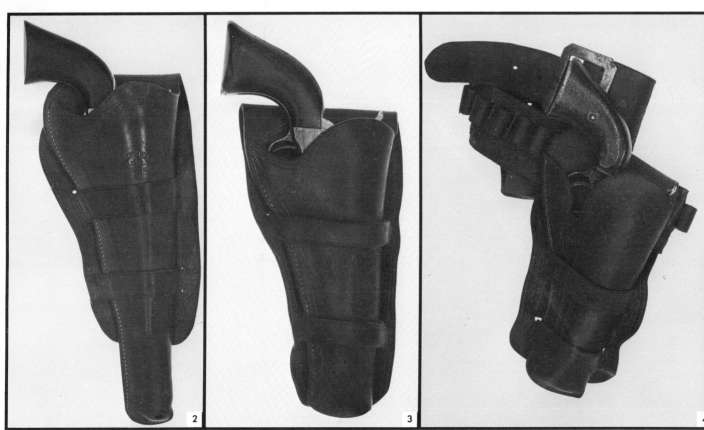

2  3  4

Montgomery Ward's contribution to the holster collector is represented by this short skirted "Mexican loop" holster for a 7½″ Colt Single Action. Though the actual manufacturer of this holster remains unknown, it is certainly typical of the style sold through the larger trade outlets. The holster is of a light russet color. The upper loop is stamped with the catalog number "114" while the lower loop reads "45 7½".

Manufactured for distribution by the Merwin & Bray Co., this "Mexican loop" style holster for a 5½″ barreled Single Action represents one of the few instances where we have encountered a felt liner. The inner stitching along the main-seam and the "S" curve top pouch contour, as well as behind this contour on the belt loop, indicate the areas where this blue felt lining had originally been sewn.

This holster, distributed by Shapleigh Hardware is stamped on the upper loop "Diamond Brand". Though a typical "Mexican loop" holster, it does show a rather scarce combination, that of a 4 3/4" Single Action holster in conjunction with a double loop design. The skirt is unusually "squared" and its manufacturer will probably never be identified.

Two Hibbard, Spencer, Bartlett, & Co.'s "Mexican loop" holsters bearing their intertwined "H.S.B.Co" logo. The right holster appears to have its "S" curve top pouch contour altered. This same holster features two nickel plated conchos which may have designated this holster as a "deluxe" model.

This simple double looped "Mexican style" holster for a 5½″ Colt Single Action is simply stamped "V.L&A" Chicago" on its upper pouch. This holster was identified as being sold by Van Lengerke & Antoine of Chicago. Reinforced with an iron rivet, the main seam was sewn to form a closed muzzle.

Wearing his right-handed holster in cross-draw fashion, this young man's holster appears to be one of the "store bought" variety and closely resembles the Hibbard, Spencer, Bartlett & Co.'s holster illustrated in this chapter.

# Miscellaneous and Unidentifiable Holsters

Though the title of this chapter may seem somewhat depressing, in reality it speaks of probably ninety percent of all collectable frontier holsters. Though there were vast amounts of these unidentifiable holsters available for our study, we have tried to sort out and illustrate only those which we believe show special characteristics of interest.

Under the category of "Miscellaneous" we, will try to illustrate some of the various oddities which do not necessarily lend themselves to any given chapter in this study. Many are innovative and unique, and tend to illustrate that the presence of a hand gun in an unexpected convenient location, could, in a moment, mean the difference between life or death.

**Bridgeport Gun Implement Co.** The "Bridgeport Rig" as it is called by collectors represents a dramatic innovation to try to eliminate the need for a leather holster and yet have a revolver handy for split second use. Invented by Captain Louis S. Flatau, sheriff of Camp County, Texas in 1882, this "Pistol and Carbine Carrier" was supposed to be the "ultimate" means for carrying a revolver. It was tried out by the U.S. Cavalry in 1883 being issued from San Antonio Arsenal. It was rejected by the Army for several basic reasons and the complete story of this "outfit" is given in the book "A Study of the Colt Single Action Army Revolver". This unit was commercially manufactured by the Bridgeport Gun Implement Co. They are extremely desirable collector's items and fakes prevail; see page 57.

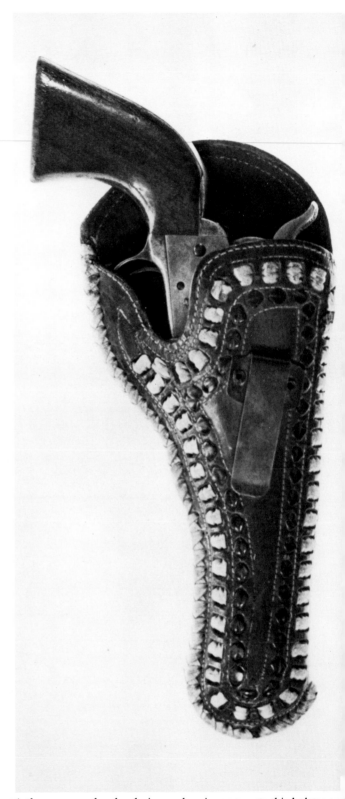

A thong woven border design and main seam, sets this holster apa from others. Possibly of Mexican origin, this clip holster could tucked away under the belt for ultimate concealment.

Another unmarked "Mexican loop" holster for a 4″ Colt Sheriff's model Single Action.

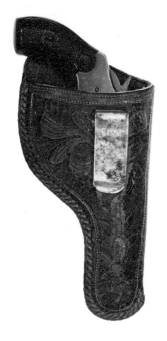

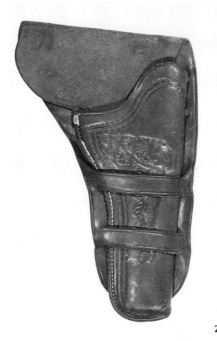

1

2

3

The turn of the century influence is illustrated in this "hip pocket" clip holster which would house one of the many then popular "Saturday Nite Specials" keeping a revolver handy but concealed in a "gentleman's society".

A "Mexican loop" holster with a distinctive belt loop configuration, departs from the normal design and instead presented a nude maiden with flowing hair embossed nicely onto the pouch. A very unique adornment and design.

A holster designed to fit the steering wheel column of a "Model T" Ford was manufactured by J. E. Schriner of Rapid City, So. Dak. To accomplish this attachment this holster was fitted with two buckled straps riveted onto its back skirt.

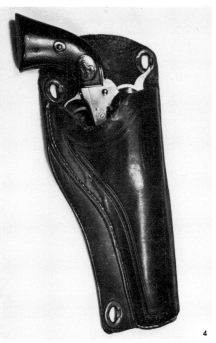

4

5

6

Possibly custom designed, this "Model A" holster was made to fit onto the turnbuckles on the side door panels of a Model A Ford. It was also fitted with a belt loop and could be worn in a conventional manner.

This belt and holster are marked "J. R. MONTFORT G. MAKER". The holster's pouch is hand tooled Mexican style, while the skirt shows a mosaic pattern. The snap-strap tends to date this holster into the semi-modern period. The single loop is riveted in place with two iron rivets.

This handmade holster is made from a single piece of leather, folded at the muzzle and stitched up both sides with rawhide. The upper seam junctures are reinforced with bailing wire. A hammer strap protrudes through a hole in the upper pouch.

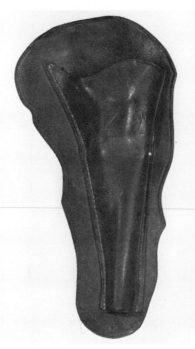

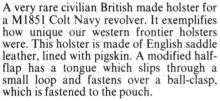

A very rare civilian British made holster for a M1851 Colt Navy revolver. It exemplifies how unique our western frontier holsters were. This holster is made of English saddle leather, lined with pigskin. A modified half-flap has a tongue which slips through a small loop and fastens over a ball-clasp, which is fastened to the pouch.

Styled after the general configuration of a shoulder holster, this holster has a unique "half pouch" design. The belt loop on the back is fastened with three iron rivets. The "half pouch" is stitched to the skirt, yet it has the typical, though somewhat modified "S" curve top pouch contour.

This "Olive Patent" holster was featured i the catalog of "N. Curry and Co.", Sa Francisco, 1884. A similar holster was illu trated in the Browning Bros. catalog o 1905, and it may well be that this was standard trade item. This holster is pigski lined, the skirt is of a unique pattern, whil the pouch suggests a "California" flavor.

Studded holsters and belts like this "rig" were available at several of the saddlery shops. This one though typically "Mexican loop" style depart somewhat from the standard "S" curve top pouch contour. It is a left handed holster and may have originally been one of a pair.

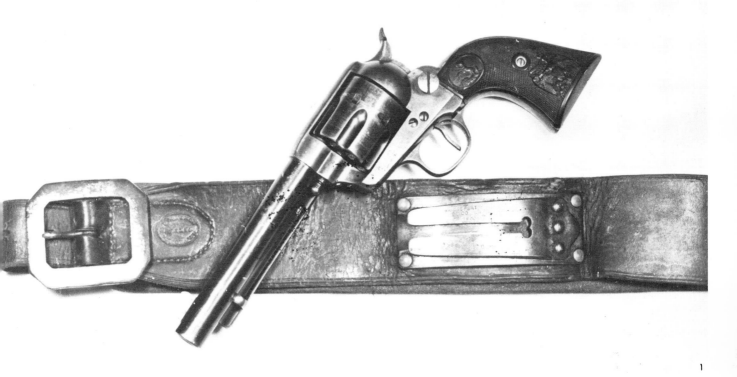

n original "Bridgeport GI" rig and stud with a 5½" Colt Single Action. These "rigs" are considered rare today and collectors pay premium rices for them. The collector who is contemplating the purchase of one of these "rigs" should study this illustration well as fakes of this carrier re prevalent.

A FAKE "Bridgeport Rig" shows crude manufacture and stamping. Stampings are found on the body, and not on the tines as on the original, and are not complete.

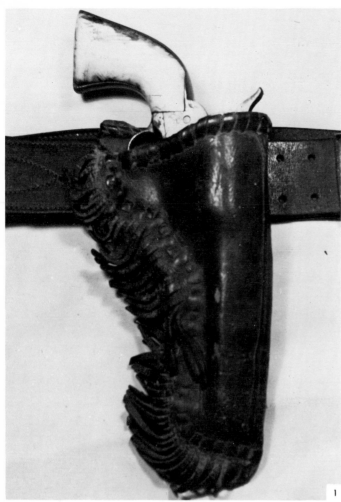

This handstitched "homemade" fringed holster for a 4¾" Colt Single Action was made from a boot top. The thong weaved main seam and thong wrapped upper pouch contour represent the maker's personal innovations and result in an attractive unit.

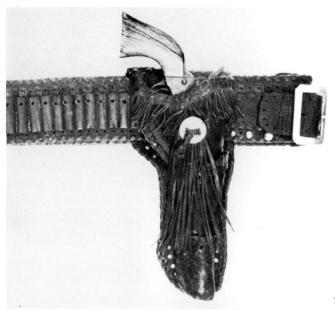

Holsters, as this one, with special adornments as fringes and studding were undoubtedly "show off" holsters. They were used in parades, Wild West Shows and Rodeos where special embellishments helped to promote the needed atmosphere. They are quite colorful and add much to a holster collection.

This old timer from the 1870's, dressed in his corduroy outfit, sport what appears to be a Smith & Wesson Schofield revolver in a "Semi California" style holster. In one hand he holds the muzzle of a Winchester M1866 S.R.C. while in the other, the remnant of his cigar butt.

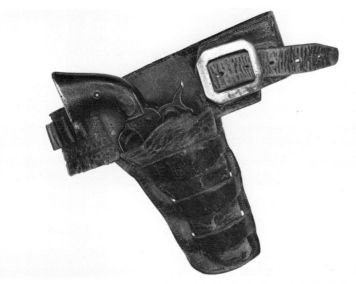

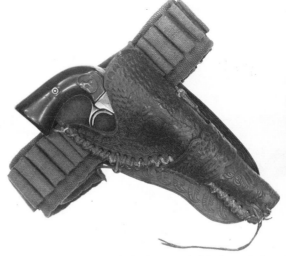

A matching belt and holster for a 4¾" Colt Single Action of the "Mexican Loop" design. Short holsters having three loops are in themselves extremely scarce. This holster's upper loop is marked "TEXAS" while the lower loop is adorned with cattle brands.

Departing from the usual Mexican tooled holster design, this unique holster sports a horse and cowboy motif on the pouch, while the loop shows a running deer. Holsters which show hand tooled figures are exceedingly scarce. The main seam has been re-stitched with rawhide along with some minor muzzle area repairs.

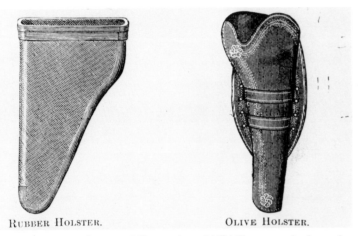

RUBBER HOLSTER.                    OLIVE HOLSTER.

A page from the N. Curry and Co. catalog of 1884 illustrates the foregoing holster (right) called an "Olive holster". The left illustrated holster, a "Rubber holster", is also considered quite unique and is probably of the "Lepages Patent" variety.

The "basket weave" is generally accepted as being a semi-modern design innovation. We see the exception to this rule exemplified in this old holster and belt combination. The extra wide oval studded loop and the extra wide plain skirt seem to show off the basket weave design. The "S" curve upper pouch contour has been somewhat modified by a former owner.

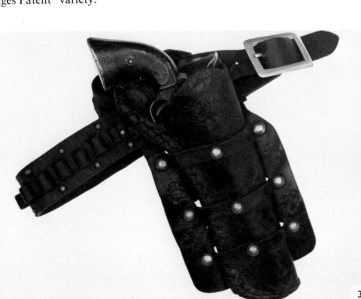

This very individualistic holster sports several unique features. The "studs" are really small conchos made from old Mexican silver pesos (dated 1905 and 1906). The pouch top shows a "Texas star" design while the wide skirt is decorated with spades, hearts, diamonds and clubs. The pouch is thong stitched, while the belt sports the woven cartridge loops.

Border Style holster with an integral loop is lined with chamois and unmarked. This is a money belt originally designed for 45 caliber cartridges. Note the decoration added by previous owner and the rifle cartridges carried in the pistol belt.

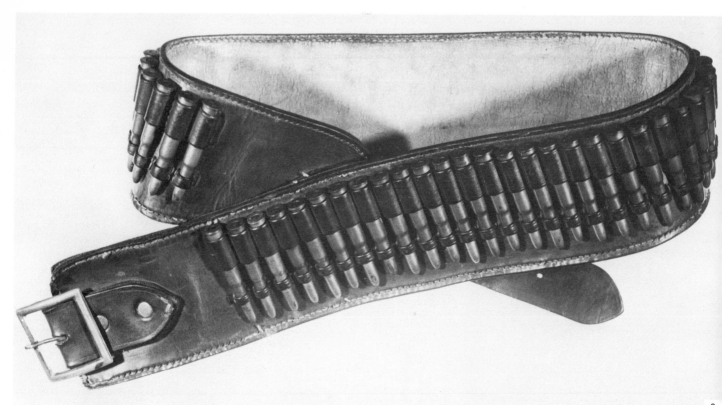

Mexican bandolero with white lining to prevent discoloration of the uniform.

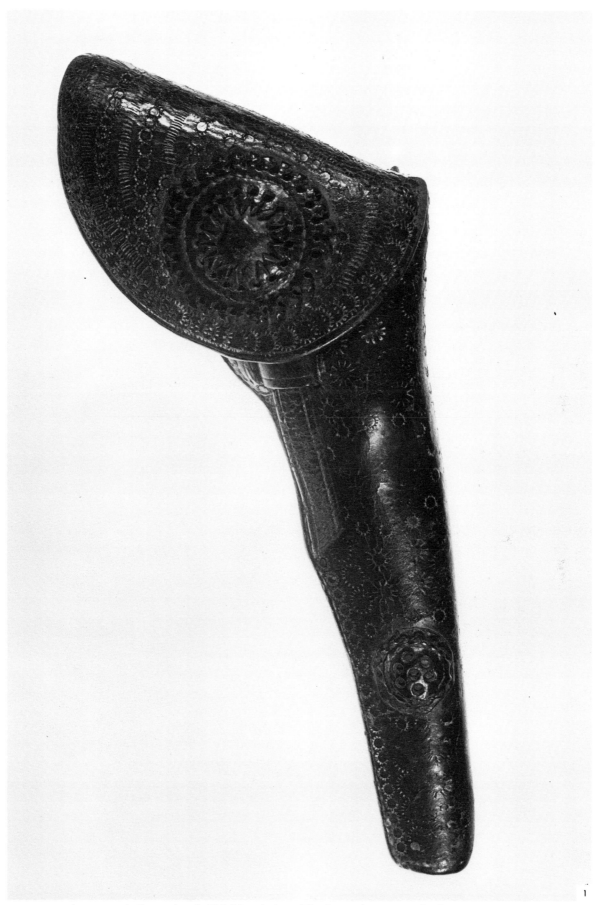

An extremely fine and early Colt Navy holster. The decorations are made of applied leather.

# SPURS

*Robert O'Dell*

The horse was introduced to North America by the Spanish conquistadors. As the Spanish army marched across the Southwest plains, their use of arms and horses proved to be the downfall of the native Indians who soon recognized the value of the swift four footed animal and began to utilize it in hunting and war.

As long as there have been horses there has been a need for spurs and whips. From the Spanish colonial period to the present day the spur has changed very little in its basic structure. Most spurs have a heel band, the part that goes around the boot or shoe at the heel. The shank is the part that extends from the middle of the heel band to which the rowel is attached. The rowel turns around a pin and comes in a variety of shapes and sizes. Buttons are on each side of the opposite end of the heel band so that leather straps can be placed on the spur to hold it firmly to the boot or shoe.

From the time of the first cattle drives until their decline, most cowboys wore the Mexican Chihuahua spurs, California spurs, or the less expensive sheet iron spurs of the O.K. type. Most of the spurs that are considered highly collectable today were not in use at that time. The so called "Texas" spur came into being around the turn of the century or later.

A pair of old Chihuahua spurs.

The Mexican Chihuahua spur is easily recognizable by its large spoke rowels and oval heel bands. They usually have swinging buttons rather than the solid unmoveable ones. The Chihuahua spur is rather heavy and the rowel often drags the ground when the rider is not mounted. The Mexican craftsmen who made these large spurs sometimes inlaid them with silver and, since the quality of the work depended on the ability of the artist, some were quite crude while others were works of art. Most spur collectors find an abundance of Chihuahua single spurs in comparison to a dwindling number of pairs. In the collecting field the Chihuahua spurs do not demand as high a price as some of the other types.

The California spur is a cross between the Mexican Chihuahua and the Spanish Conquistador two piece spurs. California spurs were joined between the heel band and shank by a rivet going into the shank. They were ornate in appearance, sometimes had chains that went under the boot heel with danglers attached to the rowel pins to make a tinkling sound, and were sometimes inlaid with sterling or coin silver. To the collector, pairs of these beautiful spurs are highly desirable.

An extremely nice pair of old silver inlaid California spurs seldom found in this condition.

The August Buermann Mfg. Co., of Newark, N.J., established in 1842, was one of the earliest producers of spurs. This large company manufactured spurs of all sizes and shapes. Among its trade names were O.K., Eureka, Star Steel Silver, and Hercules Bronze. The latter two were made of a non-rust alloy, an innovation of considerable importance. Buermann sold all types from the expensive California silver inlaid spurs to the inexpensive sheet iron O.K.s and Eurekas, and many of his spur designs of later years were very similar to popular spur makers of that period. It seems that many of the spur makers copied each other for obvious reasons. Buermann marked most of his spurs with a small five pointed star inside which the letters "A.B." were stamped one on top of the other. When August Buermann sold out to North and Judd Mfg. Co. after World War I, a star remained marked on the designs of Buermann without the "A.B." inside. In addition, August Buermann stamped his spurs with their trade names,

"patent pending", and the name "August Buermann" Each pair may be stamped with one or more of thes marks. The price of these spurs range from expensive t very inexpensive depending on condition and qualit North and Judd stamped their spurs with an anchc and still do at this time.

A pair of August Buermann star steel silver marked spurs.

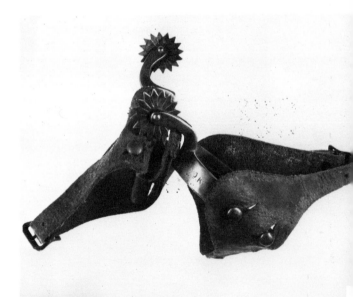

A pair of August Buermann's O.K. spurs. These are the small si normally found.

64

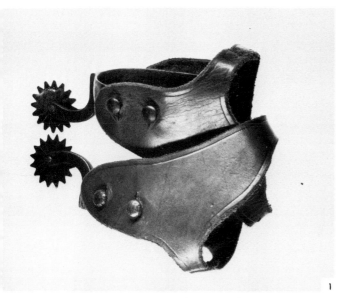

A pair of jumbo O.K.'s made by August Buermann.

Iron gal-legs marked with a star made by North and Judd.

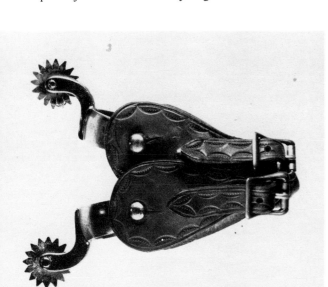

A pair of O.K.'s in mint condition. This particular pair was completely nickel plated at the factory.

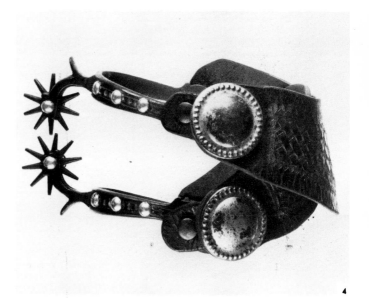

A pair of old silver spot mounted North and Judd spurs marked with an anchor under the button.

A jumbo size pair of O.K. spurs with the large saw-tooth rowel.

John Robert McChesney began making spurs in Broken Bow, Okla., in the 1890's. He moved his business to a location near Gainesville, Texas, then later into the city itself. McChesney spurs often were made in the shapes of birds, snakes, and other animals. His spurs were colorful and sometimes gaudy, but he was a true artist at his craft. At one time P.M. Kelly, Tom Johnson, Clyde Parker, Browning and Murchison all worked for him. All of them became well known spur makers themselves. McChesney overlaid some of his spurs with brass, copper, and nickel silver, as did most spur makers with their higher priced models. The cost of the spur originally depended on the size of the spur and rowel, how much of the spur was mounted, the extent of the mounting, or the amount of engraving. The plain spur was the least expensive, engraved next, then those mounted on buttons and rowel pins followed. Those fully mounted on one or both sides were the most expensive. Very few spur makers mounted spurs without engraving the silver soldered metal parts.

McChesney worked in and near Gainesville for about 15 to 20 years, then in 1910 moved his business to Pauls Valley, Oklahoma. When P.M. Kelly left McChesney to form his own business many of McChesney's employees joined him. When J.R. McChesney died of a heart attack in 1928 his business was acquired by Enid Justin of the Nocona Boot Company.

Not all of McChesney's spurs were marked, but they are recognizable to an experienced spur collector. Of those that are marked, the older ones were stamped "McChesney" on the inside of the heel band. Later the stamp was moved to under the turned-up solid button. The stamp of the Nocona spur was a smaller "McChesney" under the button. The spurs manufactured by the Nocona Boot Company are recognizable by a dull nickel plating. McChesney spurs bring premium prices from collectors, and the older ones that are marked are the most desirable models.

2

A pair of unmarked gal-leg spurs made by McChesney, the man who first made this style.

1

A unique pair of double mounted spurs with a half moon and star style shank. These spurs are marked "McChesney" under the button in the large style letters.

Pascal Moreland Kelly began making spurs in 1902 in Childress, Texas, then later near Guymon, Oklahoma. In 1907 he built his own shop in Hansford, Texas, a town no longer in existence. In 1910 Kelly went to work for J.R. McChesney. About a year later he opened a shop in Dalhart, Texas, where he stayed for 14 years, then made his last move to El Paso, Texas. Kelly marked his first spurs with the stamp "KELLY BROS.", which usually appeared under the button but sometimes on the shank. When Clyde Parker became a partner, their spurs were marked "K.B. & P." or "Kelly

os. and Parker". The latter is quite rare. After Parker
t the partnership, only the word "Kelly" appeared on
e heel band. It is believed that the "Kelly" stamp ap-
aring on the heel band nearer the shank is the older of
ose marked only with the Kelly name. Later Kelly put
t an inexpensive line of spurs marked "Rodeo". In
65 P.M. Kelly & Sons was sold to James Renalde of
nver, Colorado. Those spurs marked "K.B.&P." are
great demand by collectors, as are those marked
Kelly Bros." The spurs marked "Kelly" are not as rare
t are still highly desirable.

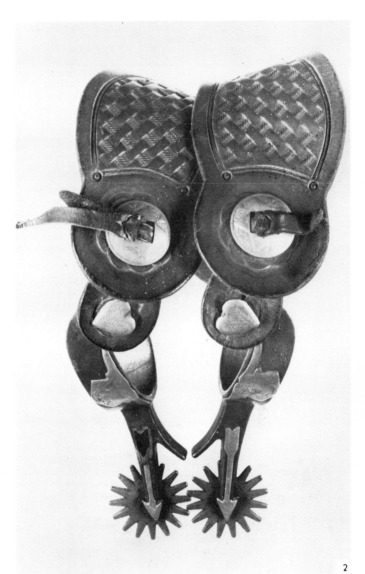

2

A pair of steer mounted spurs marked "Kelly Bros." under the button.

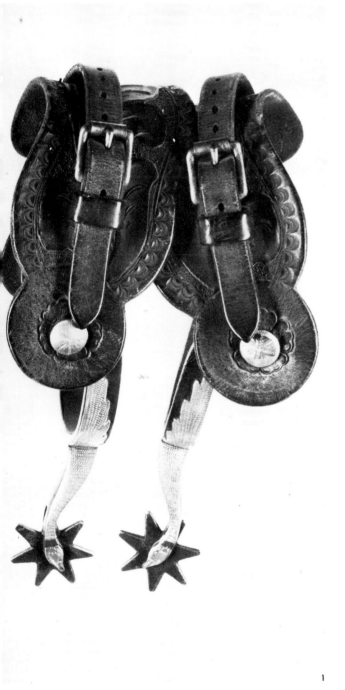

1

near mint pair of goose-neck spurs marked "Kelly Bros." under
e button.

3

A pair of Kelly spurs mounted with an American eagle.

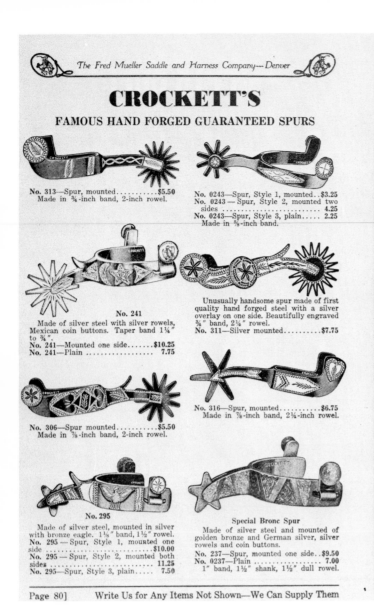

# CROCKETT'S

## FAMOUS HAND FORGED GUARANTEED SPURS

**No. 313**—Spur, mounted..........$5.50
Made in ¾-inch band, 2-inch rowel.

**No. 0243**—Spur, Style 1, mounted..$3.25
**No. 0243**—Spur, Style 2, mounted two sides .......................... 4.25
**No. 0243**—Spur, Style 3, plain..... 2.25
Made in ⅝-inch band.

**No. 241**
Made of silver steel with silver rowels, Mexican coin buttons. Taper band 1¼" to ¾".
**No. 241**—Mounted one side.......$10.25
**No. 241**—Plain .................. 7.75

Unusually handsome spur made of first quality hand forged steel with a silver overlay on one side. Beautifully engraved ¾" band, 2¼" rowel.
**No. 311**—Silver mounted.........$7.75

**No. 306**—Spur mounted..........$5.50
Made in ⅞-inch band, 2-inch rowel.

**No. 316**—Spur, mounted..........$6.75
Made in ⅞-inch band, 2¼-inch rowel.

**No. 295**
Made of silver steel, mounted in silver with bronze eagle. 1⅛" band, 1½" rowel.
**No. 295**—Spur, Style 1, mounted one side ............................ $10.00
**No. 295**—Spur, Style 2, mounted both sides ........................... 11.25
**No. 295**—Spur, Style 3, plain..... 7.50

**Special Bronc Spur**
Made of silver steel and mounted of golden bronze and German silver, silver rowels and coin buttons.
**No. 237**—Spur, mounted one side..$9.50
**No. 237**—Plain ................. 7.00
1" band, 1½" shank, 1½" dull rowel.

Page 80]        Write Us for Any Items Not Shown—We Can Supply Them

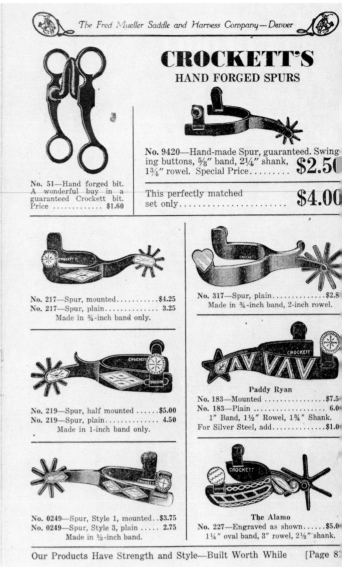

# CROCKETT'S

## HAND FORGED SPURS

**No. 51**—Hand forged bit. A wonderful buy in a guaranteed Crockett bit. Price ............. $1.60

**No. 9420**—Hand-made Spur, guaranteed. Swinging buttons, ⅝" band, 2¼" shank, 1¾" rowel. Special Price........ $2.50

This perfectly matched set only..................... $4.00

**No. 217**—Spur, mounted..........$4.25
**No. 217**—Spur, plain.............. 3.25
Made in ¾-inch band only.

**No. 317**—Spur, plain.............$2.8
Made in ¾-inch band, 2-inch rowel.

**No. 219**—Spur, half mounted ......$5.00
**No. 219**—Spur, plain............. 4.50
Made in 1-inch band only.

**Paddy Ryan**
**No. 183**—Mounted .............. $7.5
**No. 183**—Plain ................. 6.0
1" Band, 1½" Rowel, 1¾" Shank.
For Silver Steel, add.............$1.0

**No. 0249**—Spur, Style 1, mounted..$3.75
**No. 0249**—Spur, Style 3, plain ..... 2.75
Made in ½-inch band.

**The Alamo**
**No. 227**—Engraved as shown......$5.0
1¼" oval band, 3" rowel, 2½" shank.

Our Products Have Strength and Style—Built Worth While        [Page 8

---

Oscar Crockett, who was born in Pecos City, Texas, moved in 1910 to Kansas City, Mo., where he worked in a local blacksmith shop. He produced a few spurs and bits while working there and in 1916 established his own shop in Pawhuska, Oklahoma, where he did general blacksmithing and made bits and spurs. After World War I Crockett joined with Charles P. Shipley. They were known as the Kansas City Spur makers and marked some of their spurs in this fashion. Shipley also marked his spurs "C.P. SHIPLEY, KAN CITY, MO." on the inside of the heel band. Crockett eventually bought out Shipley and moved the business across the street from the old location. In 1932 Oscar moved his factory to Lenexa, Kansas, then to Boulder, Colorado in 1943.

About this time Crockett began making all aluminum spurs. These lightweight spurs and bits did not enjoy a popular acceptance and at considerable cost he retooled for steel. In 1949 Oscar Crockett suffered a fatal heart attack, following which the business was sold to Jam Renalde of Denver. Arthur Crockett, Oscar's old brother, started making hand-forged spurs in Pec City, Texas but when he died in an automobile accide his tools were turned over to Ed Blanchard of Yuc Arizona and Datil., N.M. Of all the marked spurs ava able, Crockett's seem to be most numerous. The star "Crockett" is found in many different places, but tho marked on the inside of the heel band are consider the oldest. Those on which the stamp is located on t under side where the heel band joins the shank are t next oldest, then come those with the stamp located u der the button on the outside of the heel band. The l est spurs were marked on the underside of the heel ba near the button end. Crockett and Shipley spurs a highly desirable. The price of the different spurs pends on the same criteria mentioned above. Charles Shipley spurs are considered rarer than Crockett's cause of the short life of the company.

68

large pair of double mounted spurs marked "Crockett" on the
ide of the heel band.

A pair of large spurs marked "Crockett" on the inside of heel band.
The bottle-opener shank style was made popular by Bianchi of Victoria, Texas.

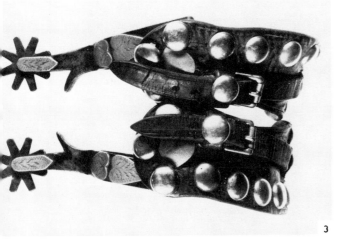

n unusual mounted pair of Crockett spurs marked under the but-
n.

n unusual pair of Crockett spurs with coins mounted on both sides.

A rare pair of double mounted spurs marked "C. P. Shipley, Kan.
City, Mo." on the inside of the heel band.

When J.P. McChesney died in 1928 some of his workers went to work for G.A. Bischoff Blacksmith shop in Gainesville, Texas. His first adventure in spur making took on the appearance of the earlier McChesney styles and was very popular with cowboys in the area. Bischoff sold to Charles P. Shipley in the 1920's and resumed general blacksmithing. His spurs are quite rare and command a high price from collectors. He marked his spurs "G.A. Bischoff & Co." on the inside of the heel band. I have seen two styles of stamps, one of large letters, the other small. Bischoff and Shipley spurs are a handsome addition to any spur collection.

W.R. Boone, better known as "Wiley", made spurs Dalhart and San Angelo, Texas and was the first nickel plate his product. Wiley Boone stamped his sp "Boone" on the inside of the heel band. There are la generations of Boone's who make spurs also, but th stamp "Boone" on the outside of the heel band. Boo spurs are very desirable but as a whole do not comma the price as the other spur makers mentioned because many of his spurs were not mounted.

Bianchi of Victoria, Texas was known for his "bot opener" shank. He overlaid his spurs with silver on t and bottom of the shank as well as the usual places. I also used Mexican coins to overlay the buttons a rowel pins. Bianchi marked his spurs on the inside the heel band with "Bianchi, Victoria, Texas". His spu are difficult to locate and should be considered rare.

Tom Johnson, Sr. of Coleman and Albany, Tex made one of the most widely seen gal-leg spurs. They ways had star rowels with a silver slipper, a silver stoc ing and a copper leg. Overlaid on the heel band wa silver heart on its side, a copper diamond, and anoth silver heart on its side. These gal-legs are common, co pared to some of the other gal-legs made by known sp makers. Judging from the large number encountere they apparently were well liked by cowboys. They ar colorful addition to any spur collection.

A copper mounted pair of gal-leg spurs marked "G. A. Bischoff & Co." on the inside of the heel band. They are also engraved on the iron work in addition to the mounting.

A pair of J. O. Bass spurs made in Tulia, Texas. These hav tie-down knob on each side of the heel band.

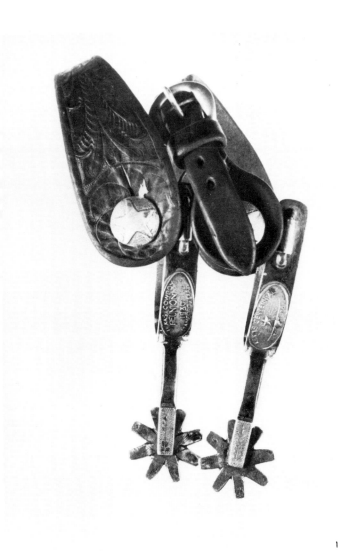

A pair of double mounted spurs marked "Boone" on the inside of the heel band, on one side of the spur the mounting reads "Texas Cowboy Reunion, 1930, Stamford, Texas". The other side reads "Texas Centennial 1836, 1936". It is believed that these spurs were given to the champion cowboys at the rodeo held in Stamford at the time of the Texas Cowboy Reunion.

The word "shop-made" is given to any spur made by an unknown maker. Most all spurs were made by blacksmiths in small or large shops; the factories used by the larger spur makers were not considered shops. There were many blacksmiths all over the United States who made spurs, but only those that marked their product will be remembered, while others will be relegated to the "shop-made" classification. Some of these blacksmiths made just a few pairs of spurs for the local trade but others made numerous spurs for years. My grandfather, Charlie McGough, was one of these blacksmiths. Born in 1893 in Marlin, Texas, his family moved to Albany, Texas while he was a small boy. Years later Charlie worked as a trapper with his partner, a Mr. Price, around Albany and Woodson. In the 1920's my grandfather moved to Woodson, Texas and opened a blacksmith shop. My uncle, Curtis McGough, has told me of seeing him making spurs and bits while he was in the shop. As far as I can determine, he mounted many of his spurs and bits and made a few pairs of gal-leg styles. My grandmother, Mary McGough, has told me of the esteem in which he was held by local people who have some of Charlie's spurs. Since I have not been able to locate a pair of his spurs I am unable to describe them but feel sure he did not mark them; thus you have a "shop-made" spur. "Shop-made" spurs do not command as high a price as those that are marked, but are priced according to quality of workmanship.

There are a few spur makers that I have not mentioned because of lack of information. Among these is Adolf Byer, who was located between Quitaque and Guthrie, Texas. He learned a great deal about spur making from J.O. Bass. Garcia of Elko, Nev., J.O. Fox of Rozet, Wyo., Philips and Gutierrez of Cheyenne, Wyo., Ricardo of Denver, Colo., Schnitzer of Gillette, Wyo., are others of the known spur makers not mentioned whose spurs would be a welcome addition to any collection.

J.O. Bass began making spurs in Quitaque, Texas in the early 1900's but later moved his business to Tulia, Texas. Bass made spurs and bits that were highly prized by cowboys all over the southwest, and his spurs were said to fit a boot like no other. He used the best steel available so his hand-forged spurs would be lasting and durable. Not known for fancy mountings, most of his spurs were clean and uncluttered. His swinging buttons had distinctive scallops cut in the connecting piece between the button and the heel band. J.O. Bass numbered all of his spurs and stamped them with his name and the town in which they were made. His stamp was located on the outside of the heel band. The spurs from Quitaque are probably number one on the list of most spur collectors and any pair of J.O. Bass spurs are a prized possession.

An extremely nice pair of shop-made spurs.

A pair of numbered Adolf Byer spurs mounted with a full card suit on both sides.

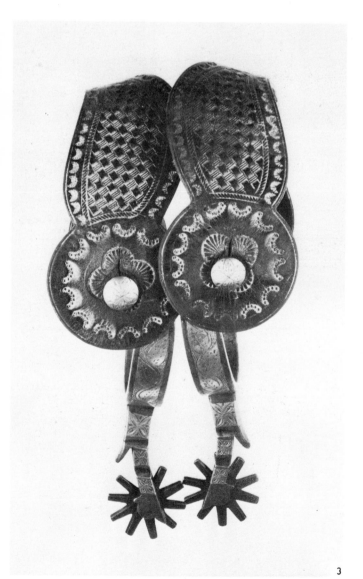

A beautifully mounted pair of gal-leg spurs that are unmarked.

A pair of silver inlaid spurs that are unmarked but are believed to have been made in the Northern plains states.

A large pair of spurs marked "Ricardo" in script on the inside of heel band.

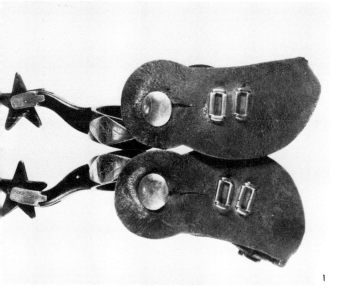

A pair of star rowel spurs marked "K.B. & P." under the button.

Two pairs of miniature spurs and one set of bits. The gal-leg bits and spurs are inlaid with silver and gold. They were made by Elmer Sellers of Floydada, Texas.

A beautiful pair of silver inlaid spurs with a bucking bronc and rider on one side and the head of a bull on the other. These spurs are marked "J. Fox, Rozet, Wyo., 1948" on the inside of the heel band. They are a true work of art.

A pair of Paddy Ryan style spurs with a rare type chap guard mark "Crockett" under the button on underside of heel band.

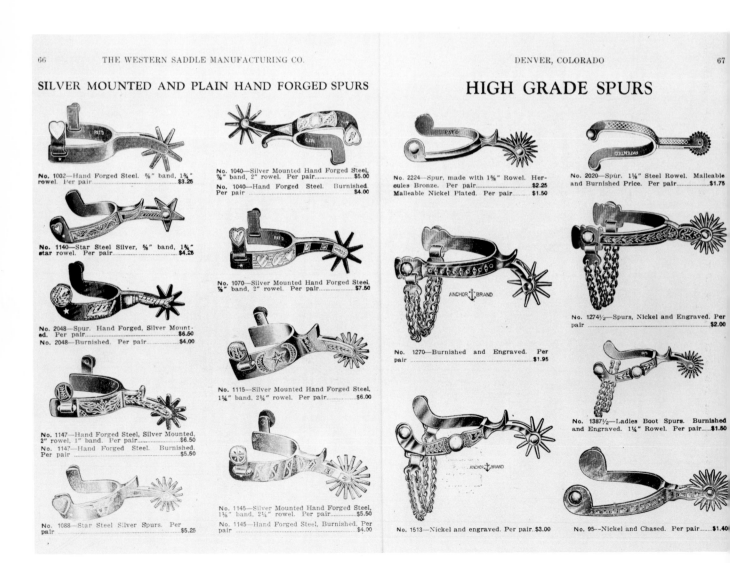

## SILVER MOUNTED AND PLAIN HAND FORGED SPURS

No. 1002—Hand Forged Steel. ⅝" band, 1¾" rowel. Per pair_____$3.25

No. 1140—Star Steel Silver, ⅝" band, 1¾" star rowel. Per pair_____$4.25

No. 2048—Spur. Hand Forged, Silver Mounted. Per pair_____$6.50
No. 2048—Burnished. Per pair_____$4.00

No. 1147—Hand Forged Steel, Silver Mounted, 2" rowel, 1" band. Per pair_____$6.50
No. 1147—Hand Forged Steel. Burnished. Per pair_____$5.50

No. 1088—Star Steel Silver Spurs. Per pair_____$5.25

No. 1040—Silver Mounted Hand Forged Steel, ⅞" band, 2" rowel. Per pair_____$5.00
No. 1040—Hand Forged Steel. Burnished. Per pair_____$4.00

No. 1070—Silver Mounted Hand Forged Steel. ⅞" band, 2" rowel. Per pair_____$7.50

No. 1115—Silver Mounted Hand Forged Steel. 1¼" band, 2¼" rowel. Per pair_____$6.00

No. 1145—Silver Mounted Hand Forged Steel, 1⅛" band, 2¼" rowel. Per pair_____$5.50
No. 1145—Hand Forged Steel, Burnished. Per pair_____$4.00

## HIGH GRADE SPURS

No. 2224—Spur, made with 1⅝" Rowel. Hercules Bronze. Per pair_____$2.25
Malleable Nickel Plated. Per pair_____$1.50

No. 2020—Spur. 1⅛" Steel Rowel. Malleable and Burnished Price. Per pair_____$1.75

No. 1270—Burnished and Engraved. Per pair_____$1.95

No. 1274½—Spurs, Nickel and Engraved. Per pair_____$2.00

No. 1387½—Ladies Boot Spurs. Burnished and Engraved. 1¼" Rowel. Per pair_____$1.50

No. 1513—Nickel and engraved. Per pair. $3.00

No. 95—Nickel and Chased. Per pair_____$1.40

74

A large pair of gal-leg spurs made by Andy Anderson of San Angelo, Texas. They are unusual in that the hips are also shown in the design of the spur.

1

An unmarked pair of double mounted gal-legs with the initials "L.R.J." on the stocking.

2

3

A pair of extremely large Mexican spurs inlaid with silver.

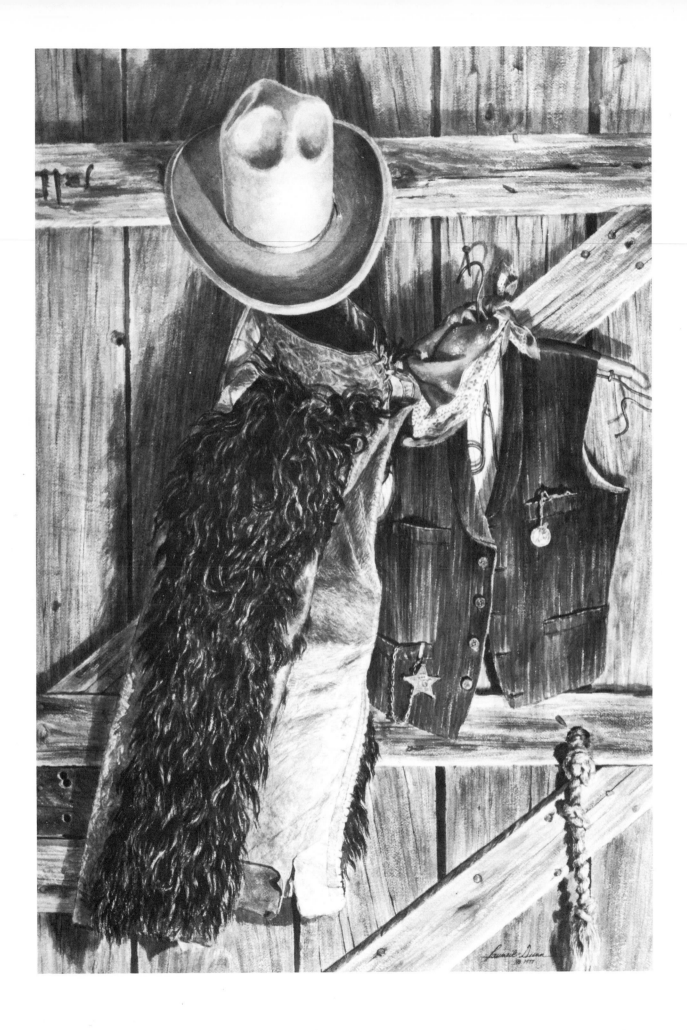

# COWBOY CHAPS

*JOHN A. KOPEC*

Along with nearly every aspect of old Western collectables, the cowboy's specialized equipment such as saddles, spurs, reattas, bits, cuffs, and chaps have increased in popularity among the collectors of Western Americana. While holsters still lead the way in the "old leather" collecting field, because of their close association to the colorful revolvers. Cowboy chaps seem to have taken a close second place in the hearts of western collectors.

Our study in this chapter deals with these cowboy chaps. Chaps were a vital part of the cowboy's gear as they served to protect his lower extremities from the various thorns and cactus needles which prevailed as he rode through the range. These chaps also afforded a measure of protection from severe weather conditions, and one specific type was especially designed for the northern climates.

The name "Chaps" is actually of Spanish origin and was originally derived from the Spanish word "Chaparreras". As time progressed this Spanish word was corrupted to "CHAPAREJOS" and it is this name which really "took hold". It was used extensively in many of the old saddlery catalogs to describe this most important of cowboy accessories. Later this name "chaparejos" was Americanized and shortened to simply the word "chaps".

By definition, chaps are seatless leather overalls which were designed to protect a cowboy's legs and trousers from foreign material such as the mesquite, prickly pear thorns, and catclaws which prevailed on the western range. They were made of calfskin, durable, tough and in the early days were seldom adorned with much more than a few conchos or fringes. All styles were laced in the front and buckled at the back of the waist. They also served to protect the wearer from rope burns, corral splinters and an occasional rattlesnake.

## Three Basic Styles

The earliest American chaps were developed in Texas and were designated "shotguns" because of their double barreled appearance. Each leg was made tubular by a single stitched or woven rawhide seam. This main-seam usually had a leather fringe which was copied from the old Indian buckskin leggings. To be worn, the leggings had to be pulled over the cowboy's boot, then buckled at the waist. These were very popular and practical in the old days. Several simple variants of the old shotgun chaps were termed "leather britches". Leather britches were strictly a working chap, no frills or fringes, but simply leather pants, seatless and practical.

Next we find that a major improvement was made in the design of the western chaps. These later improvements were called "wing" or "Batwing" chaps. These were large flapping chaps which were open at the back, and usually snapped on. They could therefore be fitted or taken off rapidly without the necessity of removing the spurs. They were called "Batwing" because of their extremely wide flapping profile.

Yet another style of chaps were called "Woolies" and were made with Angora or bear fur, fur side out and were designed to be used in the cold northern territories like Montana and Wyoming to help keep the cowboy warm. These were available in black, white, gold or with spots of contrasting colors. Of all the types, the "Woolies" seem to be the most collectable.

Chaps were later designed for rodeo and parade use with limitless design patterns and embellishments. Many were done with taste and reflected a true Western style and atmosphere, others were gaudy and only reflected their wearer's ignorance of things Western.

Generally, we find that the chaps were made by the leading Western saddlery shops. Many of these "makers" also affixed their cartouches onto the chap's belt portion. "Signed" chaps, therefore, seem to be more desired by today's collector than the unsigned types. Many of the major saddlery shops we have already covered in the Western Holster section of this book, also manufactured cowboy chaps. Chaps which sport maker's cartouches from well known makers like, Miles City Saddlery, F.A. Meanea, R.T. Frazier or Fred Mueller do command more collector interest as their beginnings are varified.

Most chaps are equipped with pockets. Some of these pockets are accessible from the front or outside, while others are the inside type. A few chaps have been observed with built in "half-pouch" holsters, while one pair of "woolies" we've observed has a set of cartridge loops sewn onto the belt. Of course, chaps which sport an integral holster or cartridge loops are especially interesting and desirable collector items.

Most chaps are canvas lined to make them more sturdy and durable. Older chaps are often found lined with soft calfskin. Older "Batwing" chaps are equipped with rawhide thong loops and corresponding rawhide knot fasteners rather than the later snaps. Modern chaps are equipped with zippers.

Working chaps are not fancy. They were made to withstand an extremely tough environment. They were to the cowboy what a pair of overalls are to a mechanic. The photographs we are presenting typify these "working chaps", while the two pages reproduced from R.T. Frazier's catalog illustrate some of the fancier embellished styles.

Chaps have a good future as Western Collectables. Old chaps in good condition are desirable items, while old worn and torn examples are of less interest to the collector. Some modern saddlery shops have currently been reproducing the old-style chaps. While these may be decorative, they are not to be considered as collector items.

A pair of "rough out" leather britches. This pair of working britches feature the rough side of the leather facing out. They differ from the standard "shotguns" in that they have no fringe nor special adornments. They were made strictly for utility use on a rough range. This particular pair was made by "J. G. Vandoren", of Casper, Wyoming. Note the fine scalloped edge to the main-seam. The belt has had some repair work.

Earliest American working chaps were termed "Shotguns". They were used from the Texas border to Canada. This pair sports the typical fringed leggings, a feature originally copied from the Indians. Most "Shotgun" chaps sport this fringed seam area. This pair was made by the Miles City Saddlery, Miles City, Montana, Circa. 1880's.

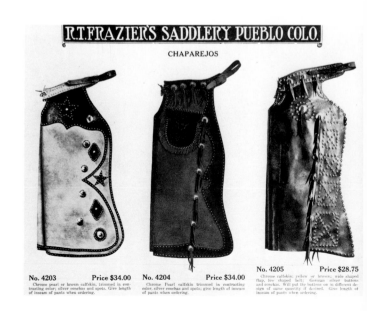

R.T. FRAZIER'S SADDLERY PUEBLO COLO.

CHAPAREJOS

No. 4203          Price $34.00
Chrome pearl or brown calfskin, trimmed in contrasting color; silver conchas and spots. Give length of inseam of pants when ordering.

No. 4204          Price $34.00
Chrome Pearl calfskin trimmed in contrasting color, silver conchas and spots; give length of inseam of pants when ordering.

No. 4205          Price $28.75
Chrome calfskin; yellow or brown; wide shaped flap, low shaped belt; German silver buttons and conchas. Will put the buttons on in different design of same quantity if desired. Give length of inseam of pants when ordering.

1

2

3

nother neat pair of leather britches, a vari-
t of the shotgun style chap. Note the
nor variances in design from the preceed-
g illustration. The pockets are external
ile the cuffs seem to have a heavier rein-
rcement. The belt has been repaired near
e buckle area with two copper rivets. The
maining brass pocket snap is marked
os Angeles Saddlery and Finding Co."
timated to have been manufactured circa
90.

A pair of working batwing chaps, feature a
smooth side out construction. This old pair
uses the leather thong fasteners which are
attached through the front with rawhide
and leather conchos. They feature a basket-
weave design to the belt and trimmings.
They are estimated to have been made circa
1915. It is important to note the silhouette
of these old working batwings as compared
to the fancier parade or Rodeo styles.

A beautiful pair of old black angora wooly
chaps are canvas lined, feature a basket
weave designed belt and are estimated to
have been made about 1906. They originated in northern Idaho and were used and
kept in good order by a Swedish line rider.
Wooly chaps were used extensively in the
colder northern areas like Montana and
Wyoming and into Canada. They are highly
prized collector's items.

R.T. FRAZIER'S SADDLERY PUEBLO COLO.

71

CHAPAREJOS

**No. 4206**   **Price $28.75**

Angora fur, black, white or gold, with spots of
contrasting color; wide flap leather lined; leg linen
lined, snaps and rings; hand carved belt. Give length
of inseam of pants when ordering.
Postage, 75c

**No. 4207**   **Price $25.50**

California oil kip leather; yellow or brown, wide
flap; buckskin sewed; studded with German silver
or brass spots and conchas. This is a very good chap
and will give comfort.
Give length of inseam of pants when ordering.
Postage, 50c

**No. 4208**   **Price $23.50**

Angora fur, black, white or old gold; fringe at
sides. The fur linen lined, buckskin sewed; backs
made of buckskin tanned calfskin. The above cut
shows the low shape belt. Give length of inseam of
pants when ordering.
Postage, 75c

1

# COWBOY CUFFS

*Robert O'Dell*

Cuffs were originally worn to prevent rein and rope burns. The cowboy soon discovered, however, that cuffs were equally valuable as protection against mesquite, thorns, cactus and barbed wire.

Early examples of cuffs are rather plain. Later they became an integral part of fancy western wear and as such, became highly decorative. This decoration was both artistic and varied. Cuffs have been hand carved, stamped and embellished with layers of different colored leather and buck stitching. Spots were applied in various designs such as flowers, circles and stars. Spots are raised metal studs usually made of nickel plated brass, and occasionally of iron.

Riding cuffs, as they were called in early catalogs, were made to fit snug at the wrist. They were fitted with leather laces, buckles and sometimes snaps. Cuffs were seldom worn with gloves.

Leather shops produced cuffs along with chaps, harness gear and holsters. Cuffs came in all sizes and price ranges, from plain to fancy.

1

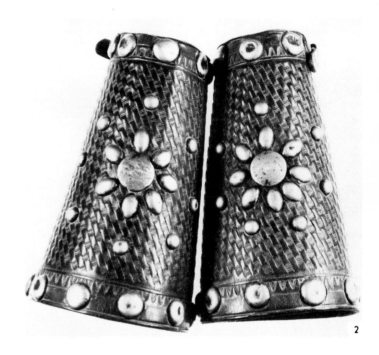

2

3

4

# THE WESTERN SALOON

*Roger Baker*

The saloon era of the Old West roughly parallels the [era] extending from the conclusion of the Civil War and [the] following migration of settlers west, through the turn [of] the century and culminating with Prohibition in 1918. The earliest of the western drinking establishments, [lo]osely qualified as saloons, would have included those [fo]und in the Gold Rush towns and San Francisco in the [18]50's. In this period the most common establishment [wo]uld have been a tent stocked with a singular barrel of [w]hiskey of questionable distillage and origin and [un]questionably poor quality. In the gold mining areas [th]ese transient establishments lacked even the most [ru]dimentary comforts such as chairs, tables or bars, and [ve]ry few even had floors. The original San Francisco [sa]loons were a step ahead, having wood floors elevated [ab]ove the ever present mud of streets, and usually [of]fered a slightly greater choice of libations, including [w]hiskey, rum and occasionally wine. San Francisco was [pu]t to the torch frequently by the criminal element [kn]own none too affectionately as the Sydney Ducks. [T]he Ducks started the fires which went through the city [lik]e a burning haystack, so they could then embark on a [lo]oting rampage under the umbrella of panic and hyste[ri]a created by fire. Rebuilding was a continuous affair [an]d tents remained the standard saloon for several [ye]ars. As the Vigilantes took control, fires became less [fr]equent, and finally in the late 1850's San Francisco [sp]orted some truly fine saloons that took on the oppu[le]nt appearance Hollywood has trained us to expect of [th]e Old West.

Apart from San Francisco and its initial growth due [to] the Gold Rush, the migration to the West was still to [co]me, and a small clapboard building was as palatial a [sa]loon as could be found anywhere west of Saint Louis. [T]his remained the rule at least until the 1870's when [sm]all towns started springing up, and with them early [ve]rsions of our local taverns. Even these saloons were [sm]aller than those depicted in the movies and had the [ba]rest rudimentary furnishings.

San Francisco proved to be the exception. Wealth was [co]mmon, and magnificent furnishings were shipped [ar]ound the Horn from the East and also from Europe. [B]y the late 1850's, huge, beautiful, back bars inlaid with [iv]ory and mother of pearl were installed in larger, per[m]anent structures built of brick, stone and milled tim[be]rs. Fancy front bars with marble tops and columns, [ad]orned with carved designs, were to be found in the [sa]loons serving the genteel. Expensive chandeliers, fine [oi]l paintings and beautiful wall coverings lent dignity to [th]e environs attended daily by the top-hatted gentry of [Sa]n Francisco wealth. Such oppulence was only to be [fo]und in San Francisco in the West, and the established

cities of the East — and virtually no place in between.

Some of the larger mining towns did indeed have their saloons. The gaming equipment in most of these establishments was the fanciest and most noticeable feature. However, these items were just as transient as the miners who wagered on them, and moved just as often, from one played out strike to the next boom town. Few saloon artifacts from the 1850 to 1870's era exist today. The historical perspective offers the answers to questions regarding the almost non-existent availability of items indigenous to saloons of this early period. The gold mining towns sprang up overnight, grew larger overnight and died as quickly as they were born. With the demise of these boom towns, the inhabitants, saloon keeper included, loaded their wagons with only the barest essentials, leaving behind all else for the ravages of time and the elements. This practice was followed again and again throughout this era.

San Francisco was another story as it continued to build, expand and create even more lavish establishments, adorned with the finest accouterments available in the world. Herbert Asbury, in his book *The Barbary Coast*, cites the El Dorado Saloon in the 1850's as already having attained a rococo elegance with fancy, mirrored bars, chandeliers, etc. Virtually all of this remained uniquely San Francisco since, through the 1870's, it was still the only major city on the West coast.

Unfortunately, those of us alive today must rely on written accounts and, woefully, few illustrations and photos of the San Francisco saloons of this period. The great earthquake and subsequent fire of 1906 destroyed virtually the entire city of San Francisco and with it the majority of the very finest saloon items ever to reach the West. Today's collector and student of Western Americana is eagerly seeking those few surviving specimens of saloon artifacts that reflect the quality and character of the early West saloons. A listing of all the items that generally meet this criteria would stretch long indeed. However there are some specific areas that today garner collector interest as specialized fields within the overall spectrum of Saloon Americana.

## Back Bars

The development of the form, style and quality of the American back bar was evolutionary, culminating with the most extravagant examples being made in the 1880's thru 1890's. The finest examples had turned and carved columns and gracefully curved arches. The outer sections were often mirrored and each was centered with a

nique light fixture. Sometimes these back bars incorporated stained glass light fixtures as part of the over-all
design. They were constructed of oak, mahogany, walnut and rosewood with oak usually relegated to the less
expensive and the darker hardwoods for the fanciest.
The Brunswick Calder Co. was one of the most prolific
manufacturers of back bars and, fortunately, today we
can see excellent examples of fine back bars which have
been installed in better restaurants across the country.

The front bar, where the libations are enjoyed, usually mirrors the design and construction of the larger
other to the rear. Normally, spittoons and hanging
towels were all that were found in front of these bars
which were equipped with wood or brass rails for rest-
ing elbows and feet respectively. Bar stools, while used
occasionally, really gained popularity in taverns designed after the turn of the century.

# Back Bar Bottles

During the Gold Rush era, whiskey was shipped from
distillers located in Kentucky and Tennessee around the
Horn by ship, in heavy oak casks. Once unloaded in
San Francisco, they went by wagon to the distributor
and, in turn, to local saloons or perhaps by barge to Sut-
ters Fort for shipment to the Gold Country. In the latter
case, these casks went by wagon over the rough trails
that follow the present path of the 49er Highway. The
streets of San Francisco were little better most of the
year and while distances were shorter, the potholes were
as large. Bottled whiskey simply could not survive the
logistics, and thus the birth of Back Bar Bottles.

Distillers and distributors had special bottles manufactured with their names and spirits boldly displayed
in enamel, gold leaf etching and labels under glass.
These bottles took on various shapes as well, some being conventional in design and either 4/5's or 1 quart in
size. Some were designed as decanters with bulbous
bases and long, narrow necks, and others were squared
decanters. These bottles were decanted directly from
the cask by the bartender for convenience in serving individual drinks to the patrons.

The underlying philosophy behind the design of these
bottles was that the most attractive bottles would in-
duce patrons to request more of that brand. The impli-
cation of this theory becomes humorous when you examine the fact that some bottles picture pretty ladies
with no brand identification at all, and having only a
notation of either rum, whiskey, rye, etc. Perhaps it was
thought that the imbibing of spirits from such bottles, if
taken in enough quantity, would somehow cause the image to take on the properties of reality. Whatever the intent, pretty ladies have been selling us one thing or another for a long time and they've sold us whiskey, it
would appear, as early as any other consumer goods.

While all of the Back Bar Bottles are designed for use
as decanters, as indicated earlier, they come in a variety
of shapes and sizes. The clearest distinction and the one
most important to the collector has related to the different types of labels used.

White, enameled labels on both "fifth" shaped and
decanter style bottles is the most common. Sometimes
these labels are found on amber color bottles in bold
letters and, occasionally, only in small letters just under
the neck indicating the generic content such as sherry or
rye. This latter group is called 2nd Row Bottles and are
so labeled for easy identification by the bartender, allowing for selection of a specific bottle otherwise hidden
behind the front rows.

Etched or even cut letter labels, which were gold
filled, were nearly as popular. Bottles reflecting both
styles of lettering often have faceting cuts around the
neck and base which were modest efforts at making the
bottles appear to be fine crystal. They were sometimes
molded in this fashion but were, as often, actually "cut"
and polished.

**Maryland Monogram Rye** is a typical molded glass, decanter style with white enameled lettering.

The **Keystone** bottle is similar in shape but has been "cut" to achieve the faceted design.

**Little Straight** is also a common shape decanter but having an unusual name and graphic design appealing to the gambler.

**Douglas Club** is an extremely heavy molded decanter sporting large lettering in gray enamel with a hand applied border of white dots on each character.

**Old Kirk** is another typical bottle pictured with decanters featuring full color, enameled designs.

**The Claret** and the **Elks Pride** are common styles but scarce in full color labels.

**The Kellerstone Belle of Missouri Dove** in full color also, is unique in all respects and could be considered very scarce.

Contemporary woodcut depicting the hazards encountered in a typical Western saloon.

entucky Tavern is a common bottle with especially nice enamel let-
ring.

iamond Crown is an uncommon shape having a frosted, etched
bel which is typical on back bar bottles and is the most common
ttering found on advertising shot glasses, pictured in the fore-
ound.

. P. Hotaling Co. is an early San Francisco distributor's decanter
aturing gold leaf lettering.

inch bottles are normally found in the typical white enameled let-
ring. This group all have full color, enameled graphics which are
uch more difficult to find.

Full color enameling was also done on some bottles
but these are rare, by comparison, to the first two categories. A Custers Reserve bottle features General Custer on horseback in full color with the lettering in white.
Another bottle advertising Old Grand Dad depicts the
old gentleman in a portrait with a blue background.
This type of bottle was often hand colored, thus more
expensive to produce, and apparently not widely distributed.

Glass labeled bottles are the most sought after Back
Bar bottles since they are the most colorful. These bottles were usually cast with a recessed panel matching the
size of the label. A thin piece of glass, approximately
1/16 of an inch thick, was made to fit this recess and
contoured to fit the shape of the bottle. The label itself
was a decal of a pretty lady, a horse, Admiral Perry, etc.
to name just a few subjects. This was affixed to the
aforementioned piece of glass of identical size. Then the
bottle and the label with its thin, glass, outer cover were
put together using an adhesive of beeswax and horse
hoof glue. This whole affair was pretty to look at but,
unfortunately, had the durability of a "greenhorn" in a
Barbary Coast Saloon. That is, very little. Consequently,
a few have survived intact today. Label underglass
advertising is found on oversized beer mugs, regular
fifth shaped bottles or oversized bottles of ½ gallon size,
as well as pocket flasks of several shapes. They advertise
everything from saloons, beer, hard liquor and even
tobacco. These bottles are beautiful, rare and expensive
and they are exactly the sort of bottles that were used in
the finest saloons of the West. Since most of these bottles were in use in saloons established in pre-1900 San
Francisco, they went the way of all of San Francisco —
up in smoke. The collector who has a half dozen of
these, and a like number of four color enameled bottles,
has a large collection indeed. Advertisements from trade
publications and bottle styles indicate these bottles were
perhaps made as early as the 1860's and definitely as
early as the 1870's. Most, however, appear to have been
used in the late 1880's through 1900 with some continuing usage up to Prohibition.

Perusal of old photographs illustrating bar interiors
indicates that the fancier bottles of this style and the
glass label type were produced solely for the more re-
fined public houses whose owners were concerned
about the trappings of their saloons.

This group of bottles includes the common fifth shape as well as the rare label under class decanter. **The Old Metropolitan** is perhaps a classic example of the most common bottle while the others represent the most desirable of this type, having rare names with a unique appeal.

**Famous Atherton** is another cut glass bottle with a shield panel done in brown enamel and white letters.
**Monogram** and **Livingston** are both cut glass with the first bottle having decorative "zipper cuts" down the neck. This extensive cut work was to be found on better light shades of the period but seldom on bottles.
**Cyrus Noble** distributed many styles of bottles with this one perhaps being the most attractive. It has a "cracked ice" appearance with gold filled, cut letters.

Here is a group of the very finest full color, enameled, label bottles. Each of these represent one of only a few known specimens and reflect considerable hand work in their creation. They were expensive to produce and obviously were done in limited quantities.

label under glass bottles such as these, are extremely difficult to find, especially in good condition. Each label is in full color. The three bottles to the left feature standard "cuts" or pictures which were often used universally for wine, rye, port, etc. It appears that there were probably 20-25 different ladies commonly used in this fashion. Those pictured are among the most colorful available. The **Sanfter Heinrich** appears to be a custom label made only for this distributor.

Label under glass pocket flasks were popular advertising giveaways and these cover the spectrum left to right: Politica appeal — Dewey with "Remember the Maine", Courier Journal cigars, Victorian pin-ups, San Francisco saloon, 189 rye whiskey.

The Pretzel bowl is ceramic and is popularly known as "spongeware", having a cobalt blue pattern applied as its name suggests. Similar bowl may have also served as back bar items, holding the freshly cut citrus used in drinks popular at the turn of the century. The mug was probably giveaway item at Christmas — and a nice gift indeed. The top of this one is engraved lest the drinker forget the name of his favorite tavern. Th **Bouquet Whiskey** is yet another oversized label under glass advertising piece having silvered glass in addition to a pretty, full color label.

**Jockey Club** is an oversized half gallon bottle probably designed as a display piece rather than a serving decanter. The **Consumers Brewing** mug is 12″ high and would have been used for the same purpose. The shot glasses in the forefront are from the same era with the left one being silver plate over brass and having a carrying case embossed "Just A Thimble Full." The Continental Whiskey shot glass is similarly oversized and has a frosted, etched label.

Empty the pockets of a rogue gambler and we see a slightly different assemblage of personal treasures. The $5 and $100 ivory chips may have been earned in a "jacks or better" poker game where the "buck", having the jack pot inscription, was played. The advertising mirrors with the "good for" notation made them redeemable as tokens, usually for drinks. The one at the center right is pornographic. The ivory handled cigar cutter, advertising match safe and cast iron "knuckles", round out the personal necessities of the gambler.

Among the saloon patrons, we might expect the "dude", gambler and politician alike to carry similar "fancy goods" such as these. In the center, a nickel plated Remington derringer with ivory grips; top center, an ivory and silver cigar case; left, gold Quartz watch chain with a four-color gold watch; lower left, an ivory advertising cigar cutter in the shape of a champagne bottle; at the lower front, match safe advertising Buffalo Brewing; right center, presentation inscribed flask — 1895.

Flasks like these were certainly not giveaways but were popular with the well heeled, genteel saloon patron of the era. All are sterling silver with the left and right flasks being engraved silver over glass. The center flask features the popular removable cup and was made by the Tiffany Co. The style of engraving and the dragons suggests the late 1870 or 1880 period.

The rye bottle on the left is amber in color with a sterling silver floral design cast into the glass. The sterling silver is hand engraved creating a beautiful effect. Only one similar bottle is known, advertising a specific brand. The copper funnel pictured has an advertising plaque of brass conveying "Compliments of Lashes Bitters." This and similar funnels were used for decanting the Back Bar Bottles from oak casks.

Whiskey dispensers such as these were uncommon alternatives to using Back Bar Bottles. The specimen on the left is a sterling silver plated, brass barrel and is engraved: "Hermatage 15¢ Compliments W. L. Perkins Co., Dec. 25, 1894." The salt glazed pottery dispenser was distributed by Broad Hill Whiskey of Kentucky and appropriately depicts a derby scene as well as a harness race around the base.

# Advertising

Saloon advertising can be addressed in two general categories according to its prominence in the typical drinking establishment. The first category would include the graphic arts in which we find signs and trays of a broad variety. These items were indigenous to virtually every saloon and varied primarily in quantity and type. The second group will be discussed pictorially and includes a myriad of advertising items commonly found in saloons but in more limited quantities. Such items are cigar lighters, cigar cutters, trade stimulators, shot glasses and bar tools, to name but a few. Every saloon had several such items but obviously, not all used the same ones.

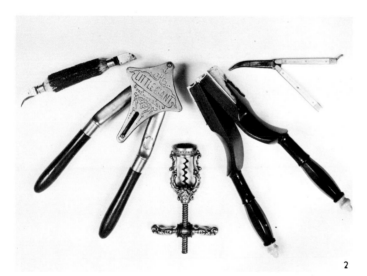

This group of cork screws illustrates a few of the types popular at the turn of the century, from the simple to the elegant. The marked specimens include Will & Finck, J. H. Schintz, M. Price, and Grafe & Schmidt; all San Francisco manufacturers and distributors.

The Fairest Wheel is a popular item with collectors due to its unique design and early 1895 patent date. The drop of a nickel rotates the wheel and a stop on 2 or 3 begets a like number of beers or cigars.

Bar tools common to this era include (L to R): a wine or champagne knife — Grafe & Schmidt, lime squeezer, Pat 1881, cork screw sold by Will & Finck Co., San Francisco, another lime squeezer by Will & Finck having ivory finials and presentation engraving, and another style champagne knife that folds up with a lock. This advertises champagne on the ivory scales.

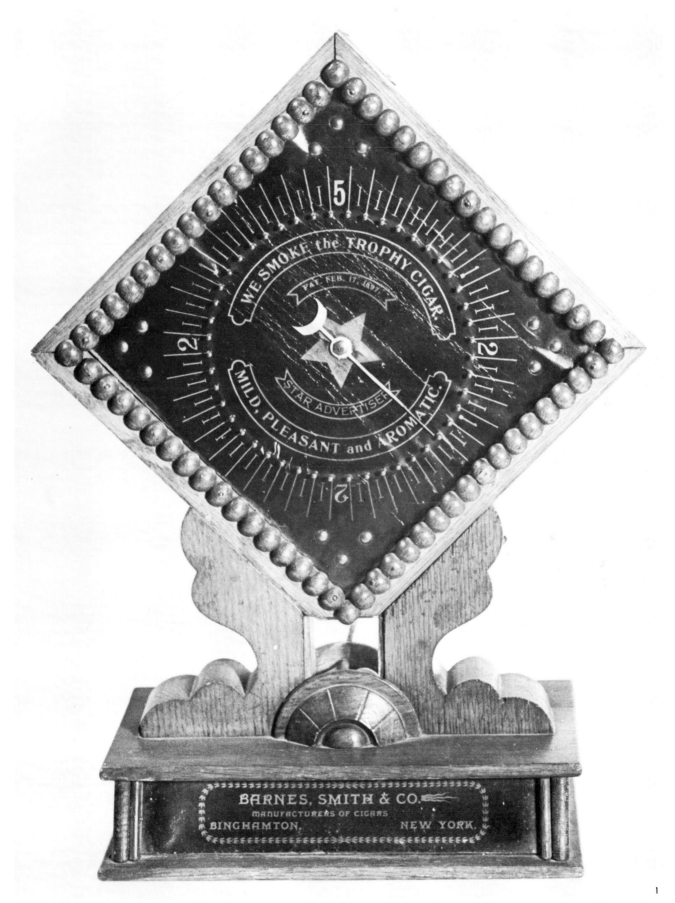

The star advertiser illustrated above functions similarly to the "Fairest Wheel" and was made about the same time. This one obviously was used at the cigar counter which was often an integral part of a saloon.

This trade stimulator is but one of the myriad of different models in use at the turn of the century. This one is unusual as it has West Coast origins, being manufactured in Portland in the 1890's.

Oil paintings often adorned the walls of better saloons and, in this context, the classic reclining nude comes to mind. However, nudes were often painted in styles and motifs reflecting the artist's preference and often these were sold or bartered to the saloon keepers. This especially well executed painting by a little known artist apparently was one of this group as it did indeed hang in a saloon in California. A noted westerner-painter, A. D. M. Cooper, painted numerous nudes in a variety of settings which found their way to saloon walls.

Cigar lighters are characterized by an endless variety. The one on the left is natural gas operated. The center model features a center lamp which allows wicks from either reserve to be ignited which in turn, facilitates lighting one's cigar. On the right the bronze slave has a stogie in his mouth which is actually a wick intended to remain permanently lit for lighting cigars. All of these are pre 1900 items.

A wide variety of cigar lighters were used in saloons and most had one or two. Both of these units are battery operated with the one on the left having a 1909 patent date. The Midland model on the right has 1912 as its earliest patent date. The signed bronze nude in the forefront is actually a mechanical cigar cutter. A little imagination will suggest how she cuts a cigar.

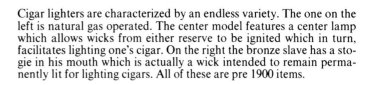

These lighters are also battery operated using gasoline for fuel. They date approximately 1900-1918 and have become popular collector items.

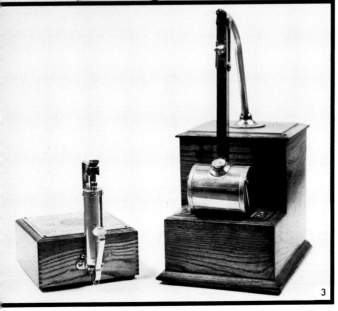

Countertop cigar cutters were a commonplace saloon item and those pictured on the right and left date 1889 and 1902 respectively. The earlier cutter is automatic once it has been wound up. The tobacco humidor was obviously made to appeal to the sporting crowd and might have been used in a "back room" of the saloon.

The Dolly Madison cigar advertising sign is unique among tobacco signs, having mother of pearl lettering on all the large characters which are outlined in gold.

Buffalo Brewing items are especially popular with collectors and none generates more excitement than this fabulous sign. The lettering is crackle glass against the birdseye view of the brewery. This wrap-around glass corner sign has a back light within the frame. The heat generated by the light operates a simple vector system which turns a multi-colored celluloid cylinder. In this fashion, the sign's color changes to hues of red, yellow and blue.

# Signs

An appreciation of saloon advertising signs is easily understood in simply viewing the spectacular graphic designs that are self evident. Much less understood however, is the workmanship that went into the creation of these unique art forms. Whiskey, (hard liquors) beer and tobacco were the primary objects of enjoyment in the saloons and, naturally, were the subject of the advertising which adorned the walls. The earliest were paper, done in brilliant four color chromolithographs.

The printing of these ads often required using more than a dozen stone plates, each carrying a specific color, leading to a final product having all of the subtle hues and color characteristics of the original illustration. This method produced some outstanding examples of the printer's art which are seldom equalled today even with our modern technology.

Lithographs on tin became a technological reality in the late 1880's and by the late 1890's trays and signs of every imaginable subject were being produced. These too reflect the care in printing and attention to detail common to the craft at the time.

Most of the graphics used for trays were "standard cuts", as they were called, where the brewery or distributor would select the illustration that they liked from a book of standard samples. Thus, today we see many trays with the same picture but with different companies' advertising. The earliest trays have a shallow rim as the techniques for die forming the pre-printed blank were not advanced to the point possible for the deeper designs used later.

The graphic designs on tin signs tended to be unique to each advertiser and while some standard cuts were used, the former prevailed. Collectors generally hold the signs in higher esteem than the trays. However, the prices being fetched for either suggests considerable esteem exists for both.

Reverse glass advertising, as it's called, is a form of painting signs from the back which produces a sign of striking brilliance and depth. This was the most expensive type of sign produced and most were executed by hand, one at a time, by the starving artists of the era. The finest and most expensive signs sought by collectors today fall in this category. These were obviously limited production signs which were created to compete effectively for the wall space in the fanciest saloons and whose aesthetic appeal complimented even the richest decor. These signs appear to have been first produced in the 1880's and at least one is known to have an 1889 copyright date.

Special effects were possible with reverse glass which allowed for the creation of profoundly beautiful signs. The most common technique involved the use of decals outlining characters, forming the name of the company and the bar, etc. These decals, after being applied to the glass, would leave a fine gingerbread design within the individual characters. By overlaying gold leaf to the

ack of these characters, they would reflect incredible
etail work when viewed frontally. The technique used
ometimes for small detail work was a decal process
aving a parallel in the manufacturing of labels under
lass bottles which we can date to the same period.

Another technique, that was more time consuming
till, was painting the lettering with a special glue on the
everse (back) side of the glass. The glass was then
eated and the drying glue would contract. This con-
raction of the glue would cause the surface area of the
haracter to chip away in a random fashion. Then the
haracters were re-painted with varnish, and when the
arish was tacky, gold or silver leaf was applied, creat-
g what today, we call crackle glass lettering. It's abso-
tely beautiful.

Inlaid mother of pearl was occasionally utilized in the
esign of glass signs. In one, mother of pearl forms the
haracters of the name of the product advertised. In an-
ther birdseye view sign, the outline of a distillery build-
g was done by hand in black and the mother of pearl
as added, piece by piece, creating the entire building
n this fashion. Such signs are rare and regarded by
any as simply the finest antique advertising known to
xist.

Reverse glass has not withstood the toll of time, and
ood pieces are not readily available. Original produc-
on of these beautiful signs was, at best, very limited as
ney were made only for the very fanciest, large saloons.
xcessive moisture and temperature extremes will have
deteriorating effect on such signs and many were
urely lost to these causes.

The saloons of the old West, and the libations they
erved, provided an escape from the drudgery of the
nines, the toil of the fields, and the anguish of living in
rowing, undisciplined cities. Moral issues aside, they
vere an important part of history. The antiquities of
neir past cover an incredible spectrum, encompassing
ems of aesthetic beauty, humor and visual delight. The
hallenge of collecting in this field is exciting. Not many
oad maps are yet drawn. More is unknown and unre-
orded regarding this field than any of the collector
nterprises popularly enjoyed today. The following
ages and photographs include but a miniscule sampling
f the total but yet, try to provide some insight as to the
ariety available and a look at just a few of the quality
ems that were a part of that era.

Another comment about collecting in this field.
rices could seem high, but the experienced collector
an tell you that, when measured in relative rarity, they
emain lower in this field than virtually any other estab-
shed collector market of note.

Occasionally a sign will become available where the providence is
known. This sign originally adorned the walls of the **Bucket of Blood**
in Virginia City, Nevada during the hey day of the silver trade. It's a
copper backed sign with the letters stamped three dimensionally and
the black background reverse painted on the glass. Thus, the glass
becomes a negative image for the copper backing. The frame is wood
with gessoed gilt.

This corner sign illustrates yet another style of "gingerbread" lettering in gold leaf against a deep red background. This frame is copper
flashed tin.

1

2

The Joseph Schlitz Co. commissioned some excellent advertising pieces including a variety of superb reverse glass signs. This one features gold lettering and outlines on a red belt against a light blue globe with a stained glass frame. An exceptional sign.

The Olympia sign is uniquely different from the other round sign having "crackle glass" lettering. While there are perhaps sev known specimens of this sign, and thus, not the rarity of some other its graphics are absolutely beautiful.

3

4

Napa City is a beautiful full color, convex glass sign incorporating red and blue lettering with gold leaf outlining all of the graphics. This sign was totally hand painted by a starving artist of the turn of the period, who worked for the Dawes Co., the most prolific supplier of convex glass signs.

Very little reverse glass advertising is seen today from the Raini Brewing Co. This is another convex glass sign having an overa diameter of approximately 24″. It is totally handpainted in full colo

Gold and silver dominate the graphics of this sign against an off-white background creating a striking appearance uniquely different from most birdseye views. This sign measures 36″ x 30″.

The Gambrinus Brewing tray provides a classic example of the popular design of the 1900 era. This too is a standard cut although not a particularly common one.

This oval beer sign measures 18″ x 14″ and has the fancy "gingerbread" design within the characters in gold leaf, against a deep red background. This brewery also distributed a round sign that was similar to this one, in somewhat greater quantity.

Paper under glass lithographs encompass an endless variety of graphic presentations and few include so many subjects in one sign as this Pabst birdseye. The lithographic quality in the best of these turn of the century signs is seldom equalled today and then only in limited edition prints. This sign measures nearly 3′ x 4′ and is a classic example of lithography at its best.

Few signs equal this one in graphic appeal. The lettering in James Pepper graduates from silver to gold creating a unique appearance. The distillery is totally formed with inlaid mother of pearl against a full color background within the inset panel. The hand craftsmanship necessary to create such signs was, even at the turn of the century, relatively expensive.

Gold and silver leaf against a black background always makes a striking sign, especially when "gingerbread" lettering is used. This is a typical motif accompanied with good design balance and framed in oak with 36″ x 30″ overall dimensions.

Lithographs on tin is a field of specialization by itself. This sign features a common "standard cut" or image selected by the distributor from a sample book.

This National Lager sign is small but beautiful having "crack glass" lettering with gold leaf against a kelly green background. It also scarce, being one of two known specimens.

Tip trays such as these, mirror the images found on the larger trays and can be considered a specialized field in their own right. Like beer trays, these were used as bar room utensils and consequently, mint condition is hard to come by.

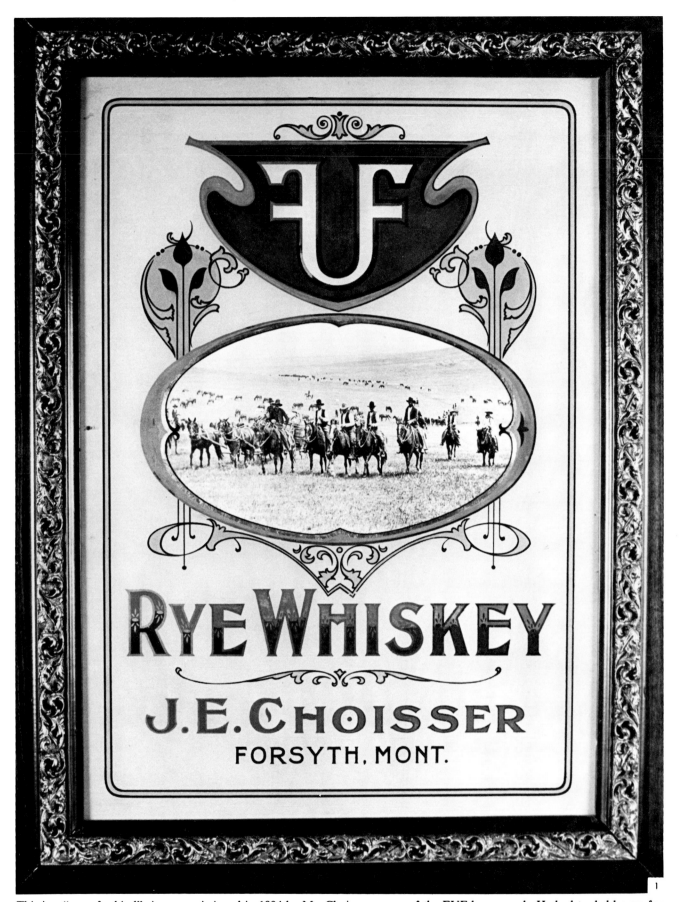

This is a "one of a kind" sign commissioned in 1894 by Mr. Choisser, owner of the FUF horse ranch. He had traded horses for whiskey and upon assessing its poor quality, decided to sell it all. Lacking a distillery for the usual birdseye view, he decided to picture his horse ranch at round-up time. The photo inset was taken by Hoffman, a well known western photographer. This is one of the most unique signs known within the saloon advertising field.

# GAMBLING IN THE OLD WEST

*Robert Doyle*

Gambling was the primary form of recreation for the general populace during the development of the early American Western frontier. From the discovery of gold in 1848 to the numerous reform movements of the late 1800's, the well dressed professional sharper, with his trunk full of gambling and cheating paraphernalia, was the center of the gambling scene. He was surrounded by miners, cattlemen, gunfighters, merchants, bankers and a host of others, all recklessly wagering what they had in hopes of accumulating a fortune. The Western pioneers had no chance at all against the "advantage tools" of the professional sharper. It is the sharpers' equipment and related items that many collectors seek today. A collection of fine old gambling items, properly displayed, relives and exposes the gambling scenes that took place innumerable times on the river boats and in the saloons of the early West. Contemporary viewers of these displays have an opportunity to examine cheating devices and techniques previously known only by the reticent fraternity of professional sharpers.

Just prior to the discovery of gold in the West, and the subsequent growth of the Western frontier, the center of gambling in America was on the major rivers of the Midwest. By 1845 there were thousands of professional gamblers working on the hundreds of steamboats that churned the Mississippi and Ohio rivers, all making a living off of the unsuspecting river travellers, and each other.

The riverboat gambler was a colorful character, a skilled actor, and a master of disguises. He usually worked with a confederate or troupe of cheats. He was well dressed, many times masquerading as a cotton farmer, doctor, businessman or an individual of any number of different professions. In short, the last person the traveller would suspect of being a professional card player. These professionals were one hundred percent crooked, for the gambler who dealt an honest game died poor. The object of the professional sharper was to make a man think that he would win, when all along the player had not a chance. The iniquitous deeds of the gambler earned him the title of the number one hazard of river travel.

The principle banking games played on the steamers were Faro, Twenty-one and Chuck-a-Luck. These games, with their folding layouts, were set up and taken down easily and swiftly. In contrast, games such as Roulette, requiring massive equipment, and Keno, requiring a lot of players and a large area in which to play, were rarely undertaken. Card playing was a very popular way to pass the hours spent travelling on the rivers. The most popular games were Poker, Brag, Euchre, Whist, All-Fours, Boston and Seven-Up. All gamblers found some games to be very profitable, and others to be damaging to their pocketbook.

There is an old saying that has its origin in the field of gambling, "Never play another man's game". Although all gamblers knew of the saying, very few could abide by it. Two of the most noted gamblers, George Devol and Canada Bill, were prime examples. George Devol, a riverboat gambler for forty years, amassed large sums of money playing short cards, only to lose it to crooked Faro dealers. Canada Bill, the best Three Card Monte thrower of the time, could have retired many times had he not played short cards or attempted to "Buck the Tiger" in the game of Faro.

During the early 1850's George Devol, Canada Bill and two other professional gamblers formed a partnership to work the Ohio, Red, and Mississippi rivers. They worked together for three years. When the association was dissolved they each had $240,000. In less than one year they had all gambled their entire bankroll away. But, for the Western sharper, obtaining money was his business. When the funds were depleted it meant going back to work, and he had many potential customers to choose from. The West was expanding.

With the discovery of gold in California in 1848, many professional gamblers moved West to find their own fortunes, which they would extract not from the mine, but from the miner. The shrewd sharper knew that if he set up his crooked games in any of the expanding western towns, that his colorful layouts would receive plenty of attention, and that given time, his advantage tools would collect every last bit of gold.

The three principal gambling cities of the far West, in 1850, were San Francisco, Denver and Kansas City. San Francisco on the "Barbary Coast" was, by far, the wildest. Such establishments as the El Dorado, where the owners paid $400,000 a year for the use of a dilapidated building, were packed with people day and night, all eager to get their bets down. During the 1850's San Francisco boasted over one thousand gaming houses, hundreds of which conducted "brace games".

The principle games played in the saloons, small "skinning" houses", and beautifully decorated gambling halls of the western "Boom Towns" were Faro, Roulette, Chuck-a-Luck, Twenty-one, Red & Black, Keno

Faro was the number one banking game of the West. As seen here, there was always a crowd eager to try their luck at "Bucking the Tiger".

nd Monte. Of course all the short card games were layed as well, with the house either taking a percentage f the pot, or having a skilled "resident gambler" sitting the game, thus assuring the house of its share.

One facet of the gambling scene in the West, never ncountered in the East, was the employment of women ealers and croupiers. There were very few women in e West during the 1850's. The operators of gambling stablishments wasted little time procuring and training e few women that ventured into the wild boom towns r positions as dealers. A woman behind the gaming ble was quite a sight for the weary miner, who was illing to lose all that he had just to be near her. And ho would believe that these women were capable of heating them?

Some of the women who learned the fine art of skining a sucker branched out on their own, such as Poker lice, Madame Jules, (the first woman gambler in San rancisco), Buckskin Alice from Leadville, Minnie the gambler and Madame Moustache. All of them could rovide the various banking games, or play what was ecoming the most popular short card game, Poker.

After the American Civil War, gambling establishnents sprang up all over the West. The gambling fever eached it's peak with the rise of the frontier cattle in-

dustry and the expansion of the transcontinental railroad system. In 1873 there were hundreds of sharpers working the railroad systems of the West. Canada Bill supposedly offered one railroad line $25,000 for the right to operate his Three Card Monte game on the trains for one year, unmolested. His offer was refused.

The wildest towns, where gambling could be found in operation around the clock, were those affiliated with the cattle industry. These towns mushroomed with the growth of the beef trade, and wherever there was rapid expansion and little law and order, there was gambling. Such towns as Abilene, Cheyenne, Leadville, Tombstone and Deadwood, were just a few towns where cattlemen, miners, merchants, gunfighters and lawmen could gamble day or night. Here, frequent acts of violence could be directly attributed to gambling and more specifically to the discovery of cheating. Therefore, the sharper had to be certain that his "tools" were the finest, that they would not get out of order and expose him.

The professional gambler needed equipment that was dependable. The main sources of reliable equipment were the numerous gambling supply houses that were scattered all across the country. These establishments provided all the straight and crooked gambling equip-

arge sums of money were sometimes won, more often lost, on a single spin of a Roulette wheel. The wheels could be rigged in a variety of ways, ssuring the house a profit far exceeding the gains afforded from the generous odds of fair play. Almost all the larger saloons and gaming houses f the West boasted at least one Roulette table.

ment that the professional gambler required to operate his game. Almost all of these gaming supply houses sold their merchandise by illustrated catalog. These catalogs, sometimes referred to by collectors as "Blue books" were sent only to the trade.

The manufacturer of gambling equipment knew that the sharpers would only purchase equipment that would provide an advantage for them, so they concentrated on making gaffed equipment. These firms managed to turn every device ever invented to keep a game "square", into an advantage tool for the professional player. The dealing box, invented to prevent the manipulation of a deck of cards, was modified to the point that one gambling supply house offered ten different gaffed models. The Dice cage, manufactured to prevent switching or manipulation of dice, was transformed into an aid for the professional with the invention of magnetic dice. The cage kept the magnetic dice within a relatively small area. This small area could be influenced by an electro-magnet hidden under the table or counter top, the current turned on or off at will by the operator. Crooked tops, dice and cards were all available. The "special work" was advertised in the catalogs as "being done by experts on the premises." Most of the gaffed equipment and well made cheating devices were expensive, but the sharper paid the price. He knew that the advantage gained by the use of such equipment would provide him with his original stake plus a handsome

profit in a very short period of time. It is interesting note that these gambling catalogs are very collectible t day, as they give the collector an idea of what types equipment and cheating devices were manufacture their original prices, and how they were used.

The first sharps headed West fleecing travellers wi equipment that they had procured in the East. Su firms as William Suydam, Harris & Co., George El and George Williams plus a host of others were respo sible for the production of much of the equipment th the Western pioneers lost their money on. Later, as t West developed, such prestigious Western firms George Mason of Denver, Will & Finck of San Fra cisco, and many smaller firms, all provided the sharp with advantage tools and the sucker with little hope winning.

The types of gambling antiques sought by collecto can best be listed and described according to the gam in which they were used. The principle banking gam of the old West were Faro, Roulette, Red & Blac Twenty-one, Diana, Keno, Chuck-a-Luck and Hazar Some Wheels of Fortune and spindle games we played in saloons and larger gambling halls. Besides t banking games, there were many games played wi cards, dice and tops. All the equipment, accoutremen and cheating devices utilized in any or all of the games are collected today.

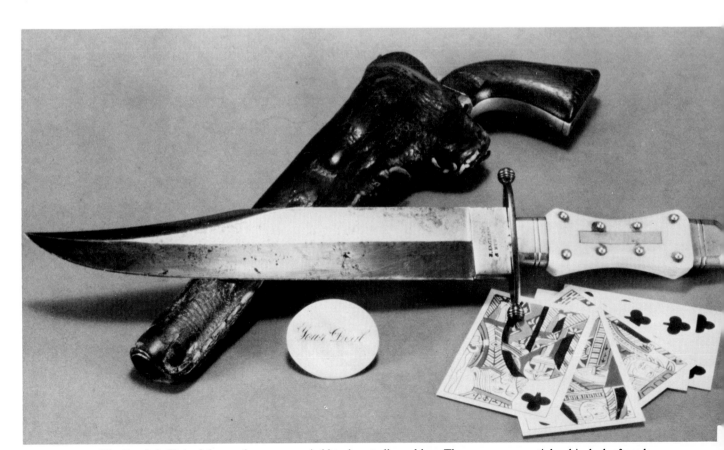

The Bowie knife and the revolver were carried by almost all gamblers. They were as essential as his deck of cards.

eautiful California dirks such as these were commonly carried by the gambler. These magnif-
ent knives were made in San Francisco by several firms. The most prominent firms were M.
rice and Will & Finck.

Shown here are the chief weapons of the gambler. His push dagger and derringer were as easy to conceal as his intri-
cate cheating devices; they were as much a part of his tools as his other equipment.

The casekeeper, operated by an employee of the house, was used to allow the players to know which cards had already come out of the dealing box, and thus which remained to be dealt. Casekeepers were made from fine woods; Mahogany, Rosewood, Walnut and several other varieties were utilized. The "beads" or counters, were made of ivory, wood or one of the various synthetic materials that were available. The cards displayed on the front of the casekeeper could have been burned into the surface, or hand painted. Later casekeepers had celluloid strips, illustrating the cards, pasted to the front surface. The maker's name appeared either on the blank space, or on the Ace.

The Dealing box used in Faro and various other card banking games were invented to prevent cheating during the deal. However, gamblers were able to obtain gaffed boxes that allowed them to ascertain the top cards in the box, and deal two cards at once, thus changing the run of the cards.

Players wishing to place a bet in the game of Faro do so by putting chips on the card or cards desired. The quality layout shown is the typical folding board style. The manufacturer "Will & Finck" is very desirable. The most common suit that the layout and casekeeper were manufactured in was Spades, second most common was Clubs. Both the suits of Diamonds and Hearts are rarely found on either the layouts or casekeepers.

# FARO

The most popular banking game in America during the 19th century was Faro. The game was simple to operate, and provided fast action. Very simply explained, the game was played with a complete deck of cards housed, face upward, in a dealing box. A layout to place bets on, and a "Cue Keeper" or Casekeeper to keep track of the cards as they were dealt from the box completed the setup. The layout contained 13 cards, one to represent each denomination of the cards in a deck. The players placed their chips, usually ivory, on any number or group of these cards in hopes that they might win. The dealer then dealt a "Turn" consisting of two cards. The first card was the banker's and all bets placed on that card were lost. The second card won for the players and all players staking on it were paid an amount equal to their wager. The other cards on the layout, not represented in the turn, were unaffected by it. After the turn, players could change their bets or leave them as they were, then the game continued. Basically, the operator's advantage was gained from the "splits". Every time two cards of the same denomination came out of the box in a turn, the house took half of the amount wagered on that card. Another small advantage the house had was "the calling of the last turn". Here, players had the opportunity to guess the order in which the last three cards in the box would appear. Players that wished to bet with the house, placed what was known as "copper" on top of their stack of chips.

Cheating in Faro was accomplished by the operator using either a prepared deck containing many splits, or by obtaining any one of the numerous gaffed dealing boxes that were available to him.

The most common, "two card box", worked by squeezing the sides. A false wall would lower, allowing the operator to remove two cards as one, thus burying the player's winning card. Of course the dealer would have to use a specially prepared deck so that he could know the denominations of at least the top two cards. Both marked and "sanded" decks were used.

To properly display a Faro game in progress, the collector would need a layout, casekeeper, dealing box, complete deck of cards, a wood chip rack and a set of chips, markers and coppers. The cost of such a setup would depend on the ornateness, age, maker and condition of the individual pieces. Any complete setup in good condition would command a price exceeding $1,-00, and in some cases a very ornate layout made by a desirable manufacturer, or one exceptional gaffed dealing box, would fetch this price by itself. Therefore, it is possible to spend thousands of dollars on an outstanding Faro display.

Roulette wheels were produced in all sizes. There were wheels measuring as small as 16″ in diameter. A fairly popular size wheel measured 24″ in diameter and was very well made.

# ROULETTE

Roulette was a popular game played all over the West. Basically, there were full size Roulette wheels and tables suitable for permanent use in saloons and gaming houses, and smaller wheels and equipment preferred by the travelling sharper. The Roulette table with inlaid wheel, usually was outfitted with an ivory ball, chip rack and chips, money drawer, and brass foot rail for the players. The tables were constructed from the finest woods, each resembling a piece of ornate, hand crafted furniture. Many times the wheels were inlaid with beautiful veneered woods, and in a few cases, inlays of ivory or pearl were used. Most wheels were plain; a few "Deluxe" wheels were completely carved. The earlier Roulette tables were covered with a handpainted oilcloth layout trimmed in plain or carved wood borders. These massive tables, approximately eight feet long and four feet wide, require quite a bit of room to be properly displayed. In contrast, the travelling Roulette setups are more popular with collectors because of the small area needed to adequately exhibit them.

The Roulette setup suitable for the travelling sharper had to be compact and as easy to transport as possible. The outfit usually consisted of a wheel, straight or folding cloth covered wood layout trimmed in wood, or an unmounted layout, ivory ball, chip rack and chips. Some of these setups were completely housed in a suitcase, while others had a carrying case for all but the layout. These outfits were manufactured in various degrees of quality. Like any "tools" that can be purchased, there are some that although plain and inexpensive, will get the job done, and then there are those that, because of their workmanship and high cost, are worthy of being used solely by the experienced master craftsman. It is the latter that the collector of fine antique gambling paraphernalia is seeking.

# THE EVANS ROULETTE WHEEL

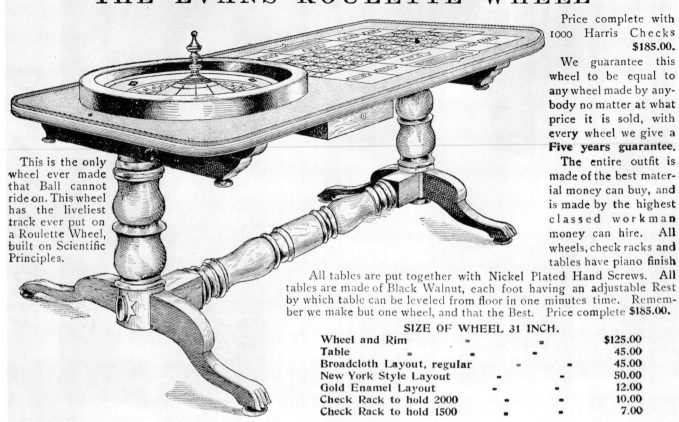

This is the only wheel ever made that Ball cannot ride on. This wheel has the liveliest track ever put on a Roulette Wheel, built on Scientific Principles.

Price complete with 1000 Harris Checks $185.00.

We guarantee this wheel to be equal to any wheel made by anybody no matter at what price it is sold, with every wheel we give a **Five years guarantee**.

The entire outfit is made of the best material money can buy, and is made by the highest classed workman money can hire. All wheels, check racks and tables have piano finish. All tables are put together with Nickel Plated Hand Screws. All tables are made of Black Walnut, each foot having an adjustable Rest by which table can be leveled from floor in one minutes time. Remember we make but one wheel, and that the Best. Price complete **$185.00**.

### SIZE OF WHEEL 31 INCH.

| | |
|---|---:|
| Wheel and Rim | $125.00 |
| Table | 45.00 |
| Broadcloth Layout, regular | 45.00 |
| New York Style Layout | 50.00 |
| Gold Enamel Layout | 12.00 |
| Check Rack to hold 2000 | 10.00 |
| Check Rack to hold 1500 | 7.00 |

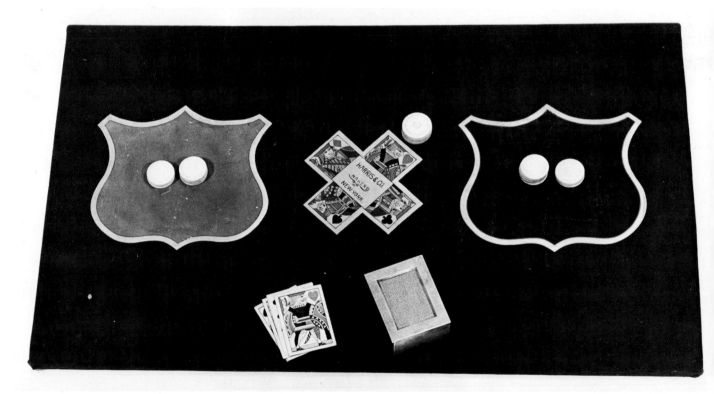

This Red and Black layout, manufactured by Harris & Co. of New York, is a very fine example of a handpainted piece.

# RED & BLACK

Another banking game, utilizing one of the betting possibilities of Roulette, is Red & Black. All the equipment needed for this simple game is the appropriate layout, dealing box, chips and a complete deck of cards. The cards, unlike Faro, are placed face downward in the box. A "run" consisted of dealing two cards face down and the third face up. The "up" card was the winning card. The layout has a section for placing bets on the color black and an area for red, as well as places to wager on any or all of the "Jacks". After the bets have been placed, a run was made, and stakes were paid on winning cards, and collected from losing cards. Incidentally, a piece of gambling equipment that could be displayed with a Red & Black setup, or any other "card" banking game such as Faro, Twenty-one, or Diana, is a multi-deck card press. When not in use, cards were stored in a rectangular shaped, wood box, with dividers between each deck. At the end of the last divider in the box was a screw with a handle that was used to press the decks so that they would stay flat and retain their usefulness. Some of the more elaborate card presses were manufactured from beautiful woods with sliding covers, lock and keys, brass thumb screws, and room for up to 10 complete decks.

# BLACKJACK

Twenty-one, also known today as Blackjack, was a banking game sometimes utilizing a layout and a dealing shoe. It was a fast action game played in many of the saloons of the West. Although it was a popular game, there is little antique equipment to be found that can be directly linked to it. In the West the game could have been played one of two ways: With a permanent banker, usually a resident gambler working for the house, or with the deal rotating from one player to the other, in which case each player had an opportunity to be banker. The latter was a more social game.

# DIANA

Of all the beautifully colored layouts utilized in banking games none surpassed the one used in the short lived game of Diana. The early handpainted layouts, trimmed in wood, were truly works of art. Unfortunately, the game was never popular, due to the fact that the odds against the player were enormous and the numerous choices of play were found to be complicated. The bettor could wager on "High" or "Low" cards, red or black, any denomination or individual card, any of the four suits, or the "Jacks." Two decks were placed face down in a special dealing box large enough to accommodate them. A run of three cards was dealt, two down, the third face up. The third card decided all bets.

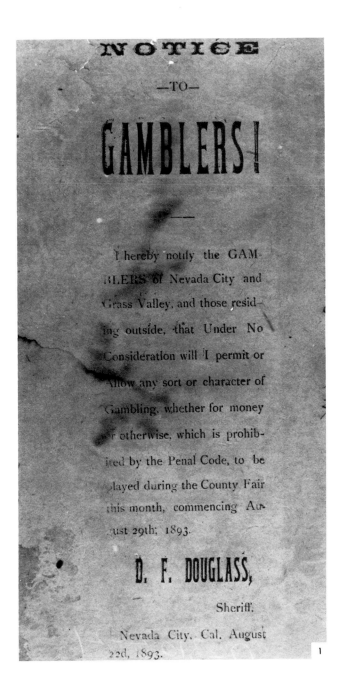

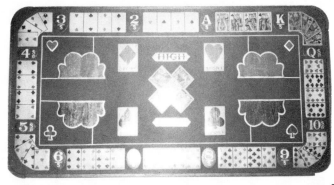

A black and white illustration of the beautiful Diana layout doesn't do it justice. The most ornate layout available to the collector is also the rarest and the most expensive. This one illustrated is one of two known examples. It was manufactured by William Suydam of New York. The layout is handpainted and trimmed in wood.

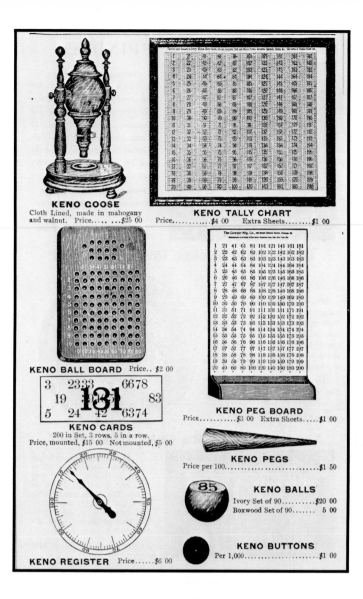

KENO GOOSE
Cloth Lined, made in mahogany
and walnut. Price..... ...$25 00

KENO TALLY CHART
Price.........$4 00    Extra Sheets.........$1 00

KENO BALL BOARD    Price.. $2 00

KENO PEG BOARD
Price...........$3 00    Extra Sheets.....$1 00

3   2333     6678
  19  **131**    83
5   24  42  6374

KENO CARDS
200 in Set, 3 rows, 5 in a row.
Price, mounted, $15 00   Not mounted, $5 00

KENO PEGS
Price per 100................$1 50

KENO BALLS
Ivory Set of 90..........$20 00
Boxwood Set of 90....... 5 00

KENO BUTTONS
Per 1,000....................$1 00

KENO REGISTER    Price......$6 00

Both the beautiful layouts and the "Double deck dea
ing box" are extremely rare today. To acquire either,
any price, is truly a find.

# KENO

Keno, a variation of Lotto, and the forerunner
Bingo, was a popular banking game in saloons an
gambling dens of all sizes from the early 1850's. T
center of any Keno display is the beautiful woode
"Hopper" also known as a "Goose". Even the plaine
examples are beautifully made. By turning the Hopp
over, the operator effectively mixed the wooden or ivo
numbered balls held inside. Afterward, one ball was r
leased from an aperture at the Goose's neck. The nun
ber on this ball was then announced to the players, wh
in turn searched their card to see if they were luck
enough to have it. The first player to get five numbers
a row was the winner, acquiring all the money in th
pot, less the 10-15% commission due the operator.

A complete Keno display would include a Hoppe
set of 99 wood or ivory balls, cards, master board th
holds the balls as they are dispensed from the Hopper,
counter which monitors the balls that are withdraw
from the goose, and buttons or markers for the playe
to cover winning numbers with. However, most colle
tors would be satisfied if they could obtain a dece
Keno Hopper, a set of numbered balls and some Ken
cards.

As can be seen, there is no risk to the operator of
Keno game. Regardless of who wins, a percentage
raked off for the "House". Yet, many operators we
not satisfied with a small percentage, so schemes we
enacted to insure that the entire "pot" was retained. T
simplest fraud was the most successful. A confedera
would purchase a card destined to win, as the operat
of the Hopper would "Holdout" the necessary balls
fill a line of five numbers on the confederate's card. H
would then substitute these balls for the ones that wou
naturally come from the Hopper. Performed properl
the gaff could be used successfully night after nigh
each time using a different confederate.

A fine example of a Keno Goose, with balls and Keno card also illustrated.

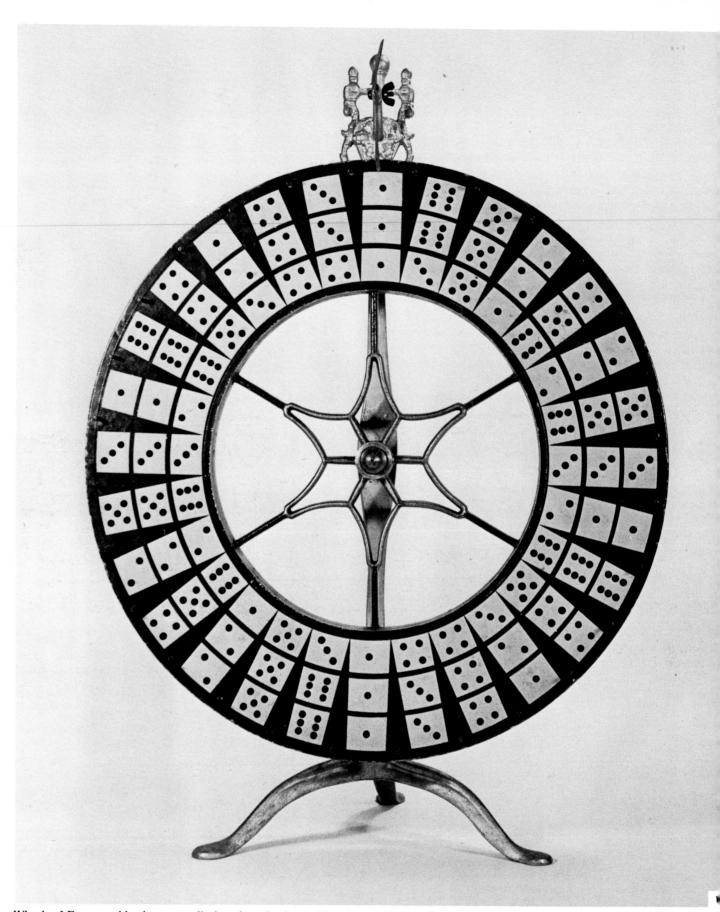

Wheels-of-Fortune add color to any display of gaming items. The example illustrated was manufactured by H. C. Evans around the turn of the 20th Century. Full size, professionally made wheels, having overlays of fancy glass, and trimmed in nickel plated brass, are very desirable.

# WHEEL-OF-FORTUNE

Wherever large crowds of people gathered, there surely would be found either a Wheel-of-Fortune or a spindle game of some kind in operation. Except that the Wheel-of-Fortune was mounted upright on a wall or stand, and the spindle game operated on a counter or table top, these two types of gambling equipment have a lot in common. They both were used in conjunction with a layout, spun by an operator, slowed down and finally stopped by a flexible indicator, and could easily be gaffed.

Today, both types of wheels are sought for their beauty. The manufacturers managed to produce beautifully colored wheels that always received the attention of even the most casual gamblers. These works of art come in all sizes and degrees of workmanship. Some have handpainted horses, numbers or dice combinations on their faces. Others have reverse paintings under glass mounted on their fronts. The exquisite patterns of these wheels make them suitable as a centerpiece to any fine display of gaming items.

# DICE

Chuck-a-Luck, along with Hyronemous, Craps, Klondike, Grand Hazard and a multitude of other dice games, were very popular throughout the West. The dice cages, drops, horns, cups, layouts, sticks, tables and related cheating devices are all collectable. There are hundreds of different types, sizes and colors of dice, which when arranged properly, constitute a beautiful display.

Dice cages come in all sizes. There are small cages standing ten or eleven inches tall with each end measuring approximately four inches in diameter, and there are large cages, some as massive as 24″ tall, having two posts for support. Usually there are three dice in a cage. However, certain games require more, others less. Basically, nickel plated brass cages are more desirable than lightweight wire cages, large cages more appealing than small.

The wood dice drops and Hazard horns, used to prevent manipulation of the dice, were very well made. Today these beautiful pieces of equipment are very rare and expensive. On the other hand, dice cups made of leather are still fairly common and can be purchased quite reasonably.

Dice were made of bone, ivory and various synthetic materials. They came in all sizes and shapes. Dice were used by almost all the professional sharpers because they could be loaded, shaped, capped, bevelled, or mis-spotted, to provide the advantages they preferred. There were very tiny dice known as "Pee Wee" dice, and sets of larger odd shaped "Montana Poker" dice.

The dice top, a small innocent looking piece of equipment, is, in fact, part of a family of pocket gambling

One of the favorite dice games played in the West was Chuck-a-Luck. Pictured is a fine layout, used in this game. The layout, made by the prestigious firm of H. C. Evans, is very large, and trimmed in wood.

There were many different styles of small and large dice cages. Shown here are two small cages. The one on the right has a red celluloid post and rounded ends to the cage. The one on the left is typical of a small, lightweight, plated cage.

Two carved ivory dice cups, complimented by a fine silver match safe and handcarved bone dice. Small displays of fine gambling items and quality related items have generated a lot of interest in the field of collecting antique gambling paraphernalia.

As can be seen here, wood Hazard horns and dice drops are very beautiful. Prices on these pieces run from a couple of hundred dollars to several hundred, determined by the degree of beauty, and the condition.

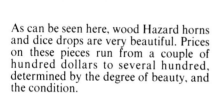

Dice cups come in all sizes and degrees of workmanship. Some were made out of wood or ivory, the majority were leather. But even the leather ones differed; some were carved, some plain, a few were handsewn, most were machine done. Cups could have a "trip" at the mouth, to make sure that the dice tumbled out. Others, known as "slick" cups, were used by the sharper to control the dice. Perhaps the best "sleeper" in the gambling collecting field is the dice cup, for, with all the variations in styles, materials and sizes, they all command the same low prices.

ems that were responsible for the transfer of funds from naive players, to the keepers of the "toys", the professional gamblers. Gambling supply houses manufactured both straight and crooked tops and other small pocket games.

# CHEATING

The professional card player had to rely on more than simply luck to assure that his time spent at the tables produced a profit. He would practice for many hours in an attempt to master the art of cheating. The sharp could handle a deck of cards as skillfully as a surgeon his scalpel. He could adeptly false cut and shuffle, palm, stock, second and bottom deal while the eyes of all the players were concentrated on his hands. The professional could purchase decks of cards that were marked, stripped, trimmed, sanded, daubed, waxed, treated with luminous ink, or he could perform his own "special work". His tools consisted of intricately made holdouts, shiners, daubs, trimmers, thumb pricks, corner rounders and many other small items, all aids creating the advantage needed for a sure win.

Of all the collectables related to card playing the "holdouts", displayed properly, generate the most interest. A holdout enabled the cheater to withdraw one or more cards from the deck, to be brought into play only when they would better his "hand". Almost all holdouts have a "thief" which will accept the cards to be concealed on the body of the sharper. Holdouts were usually concealed in the player's sleeve, vest or elsewhere in his clothing. They could be activated by arm pressure, gravity, extending a leg, or spreading the chest, hips or knees. There is one rare holdout that required the wearing of a special sock, with mechanism, that attached to the cheater's toe. To activate the thief concealed in the sleeve, the sharper would only need to move his foot. All of these early holdouts are rare and therefore expensive.

In order for the sharp to produce his own "strippers" to be used in any of the card banking, or short card games, he needed a card trimmer, and, in some cases, a corner rounder. After round cornered cards were trimmed, the corner rounder would be used to reshape them. Both of these items are extremely rare today.

1

After round cornered cards were trimmed, the corner rounder was employed to put the proper corners back on. On the right is a "shear" style trimmer. These are very rare and therefore expensive. The corner rounder, on the left, is a "lever" type.

No collection of fine antique gambling paraphernalia would be complete without some of the quality related items that compliment the display. Such items as early books, paintings, prints, postcards and photography depicting gambling scenes, assorted ornate poker chips, counters and markers, complete gaming kits, old lottery tickets, broadsides and schemes, are as much a part of a collection of Old West gambling as the other equipment described and illustrated on these pages.

Collecting antique gambling paraphernalia is an exciting and rewarding avocation. When viewing a beautifully composed display of antique gaming equipment and fine related items the viewer is reminded of a turbulent era, the development of the West. This was a time of recklessness, where hundreds of thousands of dollars could be won or lost in a single night. It was a time of little law and order, a period of great opportunity, an age when the man that was fast with a gun and proficient at the gaming tables, stood supreme.

Over the long haul, things didn't go so well for the gambler. As civilization slowly caught up with the mining camps and frontier crossroads, the gambler steadily lost favor and eventually moved on.

"Get the money" was the creed of the gambler, and get the money he did. But keeping the money was something else, and almost all gamblers died lonely and broke.

Card playing was a popular pastime for river travelers during the mid-19th century.

The "Bug" holdout, although one of the simplest looking items, is well made, rare and fairly expensive. This holdout, because of its size, was very versatile, it could have been used in many different ways. The end, used to handle the device, was made of silver, ivory or pearl. The one illustrated has an ivory "button".

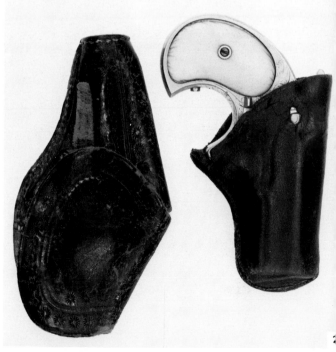

Small derringers such as the one illustrated above were favored by gamblers because they were easily concealed and readily available when needed.

"Steamboat" cards such as these were commonly used by gamblers because they were the least expensive cards available. Full decks such as these are rare and very desirable.

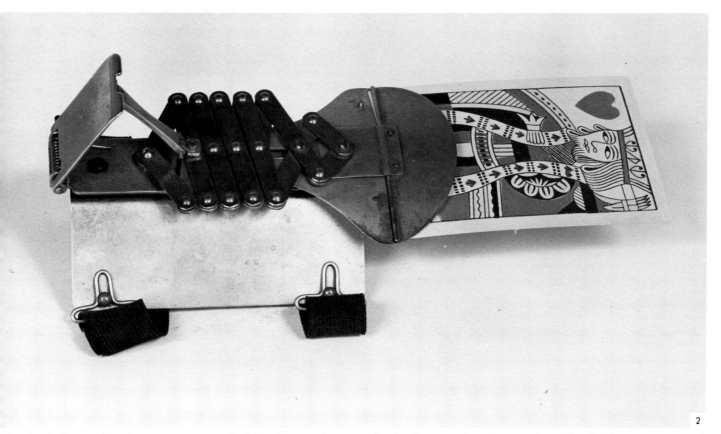

Cheating devices, such as the arm pressure card holdout illustrated, are very hard to locate, and costly to purchase. Most holdouts are unmarked. Those that are marked bring substantially higher prices than those that are not.

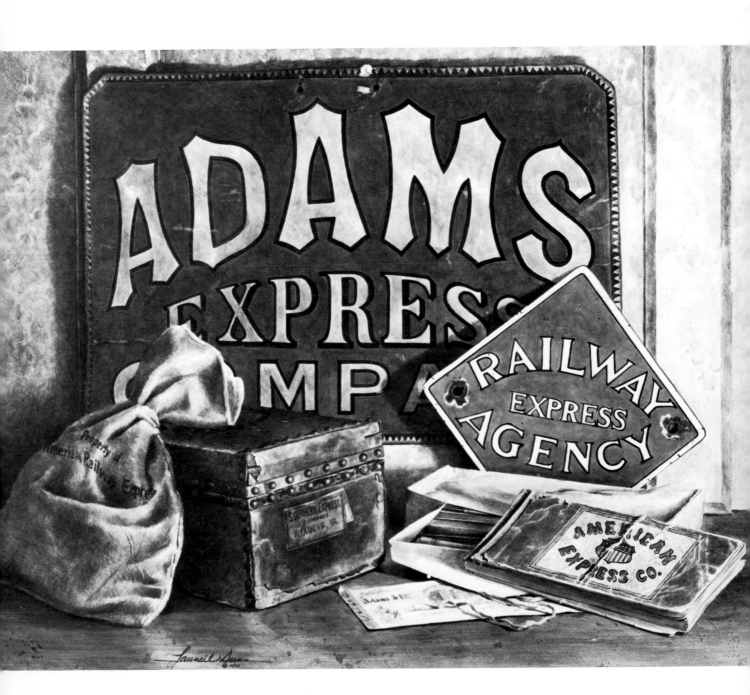

# THE EXPRESS COMPANIES

## Wells Fargo, Adams and Others

### Tom Martin

Colt, Winchester, Wells Fargo, names which have become synonymous with the West, ironically all had their conceptions in the East. And like Colt and Winchester, Wells Fargo had a real part in the development of that West. From its birth in Gold Rush California in 1852, it constantly played a role which would secure it a place in Western folklore and American history.

But first let's consider how the express business started in America and how it was destined to play such an important part in our development and history.

William Harnden, who is credited with being the father of the express business in America, first started carrying packages in his carpet bag on the Boston & Providence Railroad around 1839. This business grew into the first express company — Harnden's Express. Then in 1850 several of Harnden's friends and associates including Henry Wells and William G. Fargo, along with several other financial backers including John Butterfield, who was later to start the Butterfield Stage Lines, formed the American Express Company. This company operated mainly in the New York and Massachusetts areas, along with another of its competitors, Adams & Co. which was founded by Alvin Adams in Boston in 1840. Like America, the express companies grew and business was brisk. But a man in far off California was soon to have an effect on the world that would change America and the express business forever. James Marshall's discovery of gold at Sutter's Mill on Jan. 18, 1848 was soon to start the greatest migration in the history of mankind. It would indirectly give birth to a company whose name would always be remembered in the annals of the American West.

As soon as the news of Marshall's discovery was received in the East the California Gold Rush was on! The firm of Adams & Co. was one of the first eastern companies to come West. Adams & Co. along with many smaller companies dominated California's express and banking business for several years.

The American Express Co. watched the growth of California and the express business very closely, but they were hesitant to move their operations West thinking that the boom might end soon. But Henry Wells and William G. Fargo along with several associates felt that the development was irreversible and on March 18, 1852 they founded a banking and express business that would bear their names. In San Francisco, in July of 1852, Wells Fargo & Co. was born. Starting with one small office it grew to fifty-five offices by 1855.

Early in 1855 an event occurred which would change Wells Fargo's position in California and would eliminate its major competitor. On Friday, February 22nd, which was later to be known as "Black Friday", rumors started circulating around San Francisco that the banks were not solvent. This started a major "run" on all the banks in the city. All, including Wells Fargo, had to close their doors to the public. However, after working all weekend on their books, Wells Fargo was found to be very sound, and on the following Tuesday they opened for business. Adams & Co. along with several other competitors suffered great losses and went bankrupt. Adams & Co. would never do business in California again.

With Wells Fargo's biggest competitor out of business they now became the main banking and express company in California. Soon they would buy out the majority of their smaller competitors and eventually become the major express company within the state.

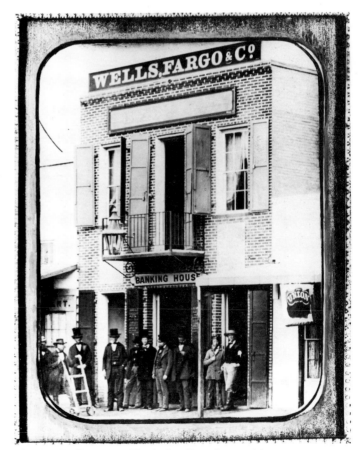

The first Wells Fargo office in San Francisco on Montgomery Street. Circa — 1852. The sign on the building below the Wells Fargo sign reads — Express. Note the iron shutters on the windows and doors.

"Jack" atop a Wells Fargo treasure box which his master had entrusted to him. This photo shows the use of the dog as the symbol of strength and security, which was used by the express Co.'s from the earliest times.

Two Wells Fargo messengers who meant business. Note the use of cartridge belts and rifles. Circa — 1890's.

Employees of Wells Fargo — Reno, Nevada. Circa 1890's. Note treasure boxes, coin bags, cap badges and firearms. Also note the use of th Winchester rifle, as well as the revolvers on top of the treasure boxes. The man on the right has just activated the camera, with the bulb in h hand.

# Staging

When one thinks of the American West one item seems to typify it best, The Concord Stagecoach. This vehicle, built by Abbott & Downing of Concord, New Hampshire, was even in its day recognized as the Rolls Royce of stage coaches. It weighed but 2500 lbs., could seat nine passengers inside, six on top, and still had room for Wells Fargo's treasure box, as well as room to spare in the back boot (storage compartment) for luggage. The Concord's main difference was its rounded body, and its large leather braces on which the body would roll back and forth. It was said by many passengers that it "rode like a cradle".

The men who drove these wooden palaces on wheels were also to obtain immortality in Western Folklore. "Knights of the Whip," as they were known, were the central figures that united horse flesh, wood, and iron into a smoothly oiled machine. One such figure was the renowned Hank Monk, who drove Horace Greeley from Carson City, Nevada to Placerville, California in record time. Monk's statement "Hold your seat Horace,

I'll get you there on time", was typical of this special breed of men.

Wells Fargo's role in staging in the early days was somewhat limited. But in 1857, with the formation of the Overland Mail Co., Wells Fargo's involvement took on a new aspect. After a short time of operation the Overland Mail Co. became heavily indebted to Wells Fargo which served as the banker for the enterprise. In March of 1860 Wells Fargo threatened to foreclose. Strong policy differences between Wells Fargo and the Overland Mail Co.'s President, John Butterfield, were a constant problem. Butterfield's resignation allowed control of the company to be turned over to Wells Fargo. The operation prospered and in November of 1866 Wells Fargo merged its other staging operations along with the Overland Mail Co. and purchased the staging operations of their arch rival, Ben Holliday. This move resulted in nearly total control of the transportation and mail facilities between the Missouri River and the Pacific Coast. This proved once again that Wells Fargo was truly here to stay.

The intended prize of all stage coach robbers. Wells Fargo Treasure Boxes came in several sizes, they were usually green, and were all made with this sturdy construction. Note the dovetailed sides and reinforced corners. Approx. size 12″ x 24″ x 12″. Circa — 1890's.

Agents of W., F. & Co. will not post this circular, but place them in the hands of your local and county officers, and reliable citizens in your region. Officers and citizens receiving them are respectfully requested to preserve them for future reference.

Agents WILL PRESERVE a copy on file in their office.

# $800.00 Reward!
# ARREST STAGE ROBBER!

### 1.

On the 3d of August, 1877, the stage from Fort Ross to Russian River was stopped by one man, who took from the Express box about $300, coin, and a check for $305.52, on Grangers' Bank of San Francisco, in favor of Fisk Bros. The Mail was also robbed. On one of the Way Bills left with the box the Robber wrote as follows:—

"I've labored long and hard for bread—
For honor and for riches—
But on my corns too long you've trod,
You fine haired sons of bitches.
BLACK BART, the P o 8.

Driver, give my respects to our friend, the other driver; but I really had a notion to hang my old disguise hat on his weather eye." (fac simile.)

It is believed that he went to the Town of Guerneville about daylight next morning.

### 2.

About one year after above robbery, July 25th, 1878, the Stage from Quincy to Oroville was stopped by one man, and W., F. & Co's box robbed of $379, coin, one Diamond Ring, (said to be worth $200) one Silver Watch, valued at $25. The Mail was also robbed. In the box, when found next day, was the following, (fac simile):—

Of all the stage robbers to have raised a gun to stop a stage, none can surpass the unique style of Black Bart. His real name was Charles Boles, a well heeled San Franciscan who traveled alone on foot, over steep terrain in the Sierra Nevada Mountains of California. He enjoyed leaving crudely scrawled notes at the scenes of his robberies.

Wells Fargo often showed its appreciation to employees who went beyond the call of duty. They usually presented them with a gold inscribed pocket watch for their fearless conduct. But in this case, a nickel plated and engraved Henry rifle, with a silver plaque inset into the stock with scene of the robbery would do just fine. It was presented to Stephen Venard in 1866.

# Highwaymen

The problems involved in running such a large empire on wheels were enormous. Not only were they constantly fighting Indians and the elements, but they were always the target of highwaymen. One such character who has gained immortality was Black Bart. He traveled alone, on foot, over the steep terrain of the Sierra Nevada Mountains of California, living on crackers and beef jerky. His tools of the trade included a linen duster (overcoat), a flour sack for a mask, and a shotgun, which it is said was never loaded. He was a craftsman at his trade, as he relieved twenty-seven stage coaches of their treasure boxes between July of 1875 and Nov. of 1883. In all of these robberies he left no clues, but instead would leave crudely scrawled bits of poetry at the scene.

On July 25, 1878 the stage from Quincy to Oroville was robbed. In the treasure box, when found the next day, was the following note:

*Here I lay me down to sleep*
*to wait the coming morrow*
*perhaps success, perhaps defeat*
*and everlasting sorrow*
*I've labored long and hard for bread*
*for honor and for riches*
*But on my corns too long you've trod*
*you fine haired sons of bitches*
*Let come what will I'll try it on*
*My condition can't be worse*
*But if there's money in that box*
*'Tis money in my purse"*

(Signed)      Black Bart
The PO 8 (poet)

But all good things must come to an end. On Nov. 3, 1883 he robbed the Sonora to Milton stage. Ironically, he chose this same stage for his first robbery. All went as planned, but he accidentally dropped his handkerchief at the scene, which bore his laundry mark — "FX07". This gave James Hume, Chief of Detectives for Wells Fargo, the clue he had long been looking for. Hume, after checking every laundry in San Francisco, finally found one which told him that the man who had eluded him for nearly eight years was one Charles E. Boles, a man who appeared to be a fairly well to do San Franciscan. He was convicted and sentenced to eight years at San Quentin. He was released early for good behavior, and was never seen again. This dedicated detective work proved again the phrase that became synonymous with the company — "Wells Fargo Never Forgets". Wells Fargo's losses to highwaymen were staggering, but no one who entrusted their money to them ever lost a cent.

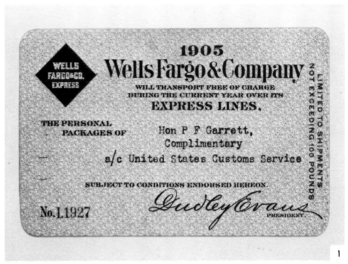

Other desirable Wells Fargo items, which are available today include passes and business cards. Passes were given out to people whom Wells Fargo did business with. Note the 1905 pass given to Pat Garrett, the Sheriff who killed "Billy The Kid".

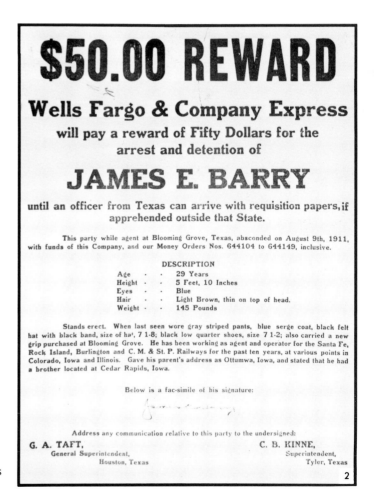

Reward Posters are highly prized items. This one issued by Wells Fargo in Texas in 1911 is an exceptionally nice one.

To save money Wells Fargo purchased surplus .45 caliber U.S. Model Smith & Wesson Schofields from Bannerman in N.Y. The barrels were c▮ down from 7″ to 5½″. They were marked by Wells Fargo, probably in their supply dept. in N.Y. The serial number of the gun was also stampe▮ on after the Wells Fargo name, and it became Wells Fargo's property number as well. This is a first model serial #164.

Authentic Wells Fargo Shotguns have long been collected. One of the easiest to authenticate are Ithica shotguns. These were factory marked an▮ letters can still be obtained on them. Most were engraved "W. F. & CO. EX. #____". The number on this one was stamped out, probably by t▮ express co.

# Pony Express

Another symbol which typified the American West as much as the stagecoach was the Pony Express, and Wells Fargo played an important role in it too. Originally started in April of 1860 as a private business venture by the Central Overland California and Pikes Peak Express Co. it soon became heavily indebted. A government contract in 1861 providing for a Pony Express was not awarded to the Central Overland California and Pikes Peak Express Co. but rather to the Overland Mail Co., by this time under the control of Wells Fargo. This contract gave the Overland Mail Co. until July of 1861 to start operations on the Central Route. In the meantime Wells Fargo independently operated the Western leg of the Pony Express.

By October of 1861 the Transcontinental Telegraph had been completed and the Pony Express was terminated. Wells Fargo however, continued to operate its own Pony Express between Virginia City, Nevada and Sacramento, California until 1865. Although it lasted only eighteen months, it left a mark in Western folklore which time will not erase.

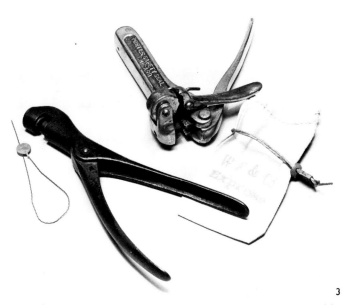

3

Sealing devices used by Wells Fargo. (Top) Porter seals were used for sealing coin bags with a twine and lead seal that went around the neck of the coin bag. The twine would pull the lead tight around the bag, then the lead was crimped in the teeth of the seal, leaving Wells Fargo's seal and location. This one was used by train messengers between San Francisco and Goldfield, Nevada. The bottom seal is called a lead sealer and was used to seal the steel messengers safes, as well as for sealing Wells Fargo pad locks. (See Locks) This style is still used today by local gas co.'s. Circa — 1880-1915.

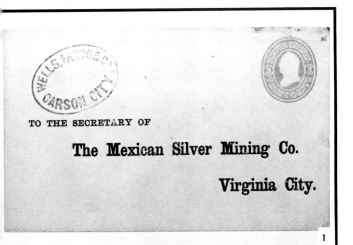

1

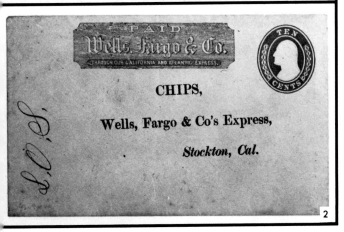

2

Another service provided by Wells Fargo until 1895 was carrying mail. Note the one addressed to "Chips" — Wells Fargo & Co. Express Stockton, Calif. "Chips" whose real name was Pillsbury Hodgkins was a messenger for Wells Fargo out of Stockton, Calif. In the early days he was a carpenter aboard sailing ships, thus the nickname — "Chips".

4

One of the most personalized of all express co. items are wax seals. Every town which had an express office had at least two seals. The two on right are a set from Coyote, Calif. The Public Use seal was used by the public and would only assure that the package had not been tampered with, but would not guarantee its contents. The Wells Fargo seal was used by the agent, and should a loss arise, the express co. would stand the loss. This seal was used only after the agent had counted the contents of the package. Circa — 1870-1915.

Two variations of Wells Fargo locks. The one at right is all steel and has a hole in the shackle through which a lead seal could be inserted to insure that the lock had not been tampered with. The other is brass and is marked on the back. Both have cast lettering. Note the railroad type key for the lock on right.

These bronze bull dog heads marked American Express Co., Kansas City, were used on top of the tellers' cages as trim. The Bull Dog has been the symbol of strength and security for the express company from the earliest times. Circa — 1890's.

## The Railroad

By the end of the 1860's Wells Fargo saw a dark cloud [on] the horizon, the rapidly approaching Transcontinen[tal] Railroad. They realized that with the driving of the [Go]lden Spike at Promontory Point, Utah on May 10, [18]69 that their days of a staging empire were rapidly [com]ing to a close. Wells Fargo was always aware of the [nee]d to keep pace with the times. They would have to [ma]ke a change from stagecoach to the iron rail. But first [the]y would have to obtain a contract with the railroads. [In] October of 1869 they hammered out what was later to [be] known as "The Treaty of Omaha". This treaty pro[vid]ed Wells Fargo with the needed contracts to carry [the]ir express business by rail. It would also open a new [era] of expansion and prosperity. The company now had [ne]arly five hundred agencies. It would grow to nearly [do]minate the express business in America. It would also [be] a network of agencies that would include Europe [an]d the Orient.

## The Last 75 Years

The company would continue to operate its banking [an]d express business under one roof until 1906, when [th]e two were separated. The banking operation would [co]ntinue to grow in California, and is today the elev[en]th largest bank in the United States. The express [co]mpany would continue until 1918, when under a [pr]esidential order, in an effort to help end World War I, [th]e four major express companies; The American, The [Ad]ams, The Southern, and Wells Fargo were merged [in]to one company known as the American Railway Ex[pr]ess Co. This company would continue under that name until 1929 when it became the Railway Express Agency. In 1960 its name was changed again to R.E.A. Express, and in 1975 it finally went bankrupt. This brought a sad end to an industry which contributed much to the growth and development of America and the West. Unfortunately, we realized too late, that the express business was an endangered species.

## Collecting

In the collecting of express company artifacts one will find many varieties of items. Of special interest are signs, firearms, treasure boxes, locks, hat badges, etc. There is also a tremendous interest in express co. paper items, such as waybills, receipts, and reward posters.

It is interesting to note that much of this material can still be purchased at a very reasonable cost. Especially when compared to other western collectables, such as Colts or Winchesters.

It is said that to copy someone or something is the highest form of flattery. This being the case, then express company artifacts must surely be held in high regard. Unfortunately, there are those among us who are motivated more by profits than their sincere interest in history. This is evident when one sees all the reproductions around. However, by reading and studying original items one enhances his chances of finding an original collector's item.

The author realizes that he has only touched on a few of the express companies that have operated in the United States. Space does not allow us to cover all of them. These companies were chosen because of the important role they played in the development of the West, as well as for their collectability today.

Shoulder bags or haversacks were used by express messengers and drivers to carry valuables. Most were leather and canvas. Circa — 1900-1915.

# Wells Fargo & Co. Express

The Wells Fargo wooden sign which is approx. 6′ long, was according to official instructions, "to be on every railroad depot and in plain sight [of] all passengers". These signs along with glass signs had the smallest survival rate due to the nature of their construction. There are several vari[a]tions of these wooden signs, and all are highly prized.

A collector's dream! The express offices at the Pan American Exposition, Buffalo, N.Y. Circa — 1900. Note the signs going up the back walls

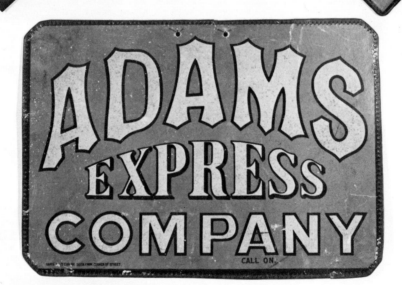

Call card signs from all express co's are very desirable. Most were heavy cardboard with metal rims. These signs were distributed by the express co's to local merchants. When the express co. driver saw one hanging in front of a store, he would stop and "call" on the merchant. Thus the name "call card" meaning — call on me. **The Wells Fargo call card on the left is a fake.** Note the different styles of lettering. The Adams Express sign reads lower left "Hang so it can be seen from corner of street", and lower right "call on".

Other collectable signs of the express co's include porcelain money order signs. Nearly all the express co's by 1900 offered money orders a[nd] their signs were as varied as were the co's and the areas they serviced. Shown above is an Adams Express Co. money order sign of green a[nd] white porcelain. Circa — 1900. Also a blue and white Wells Fargo money order porcelain sign. Circa — 1910. Both are approx. 10" x 14".

# AMERICAN EXPRESS CO.
## Money Orders
## Foreign Checks
## Travelers Cheques
## Letters of Credit and
## Transfers by Telegraph.

The blue and white American Express Co. sign, circa 1905, offered its customers nearly every service available.

A company, though late, whose porcelain signs are hard to find is American Railway Express. This co. only lasted 11 years by that name. This sign is approx. 9" x 9", and s red, white and green.

Railway Express Agency porcelain signs (9" x 9") like these were mainly used on the baggage wagons around the depots or offices. Note the black lettering. This was found to be hard to read and was soon changed to the style on the right. Left: Circa 1929-1930. Right: 1930-1950.

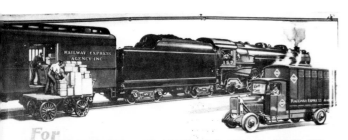

Lithographed advertisements from express co's are very collectable. This one put out in the early 1930's is multicolored on tin. It would have hung in the express office.

The Western Union sign was blue and white enamel and was double faced.

This beautiful Wells Fargo sign was done in blue and white enamel. A similar sign has been reproduced substituting the word "stagecoach" for "express".

Souvenirs from the World's Columbian Exposition in Chicago — 1893. Wells Fargo's exhibit of OLD historical items was mind boggling. Such items as Black Bart's valise and an "old" Wells Fargo wooden sign were only two of the 173 items on display. The catalogue was given to anyone visiting the display. The coin, holder, and envelope were given to every Wells Fargo employee who visited the exhibit. The holder and envelope are rare today, as most kept the coin and threw the rest away.

The hats of expressmen! These include, aluminum, nickled brass, celluloid and lithographed hat badges. Note the conductors' style hats. Circa — 1900-1910.

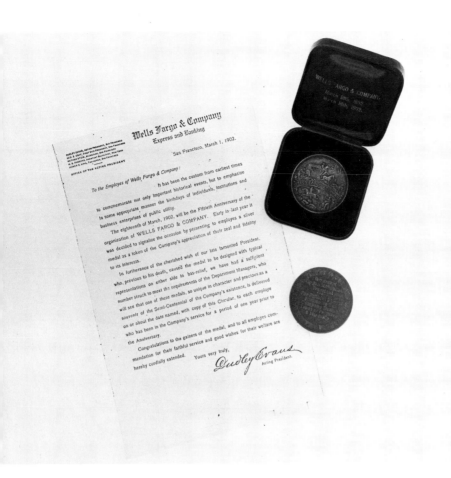

Wells Fargo commemorated its 50th year in business (1902) by giving every employee with 1 or more years of service a cased silver medal and letter. Like the Columbian souvenir coin, most kept the medal and threw the box and letter away. These items today are rarer than the coin. Pictured (Below) is a fake coin although not marked as such, that was an attempt to copy the 50 year medallion. These are brass and read — "For Faithful and Loyal Service to the Co. During Times of Pressure and Hardship".

1

<table>
<tr><td colspan="2">Form No. 86.</td><td colspan="2">ADAMS EXPRESS COMPANY, N. E. DIVISION.</td></tr>
</table>

Form
No. 86. **ADAMS EXPRESS COMPANY, N. E. DIVISION.**

Bill for Collection, - $_____

Charges for returning Money, $_____

Total Amount, - $_____

**C.O.D.**

No._____

Hartford, Conn._____ 188

On Army 45/ Pistols
U.S. Government
1885.

For Colt's Patent Fire Arms M'f'g Co.,

HARTFORD, CONN.

When Presented,_____

When Paid,_____

Goods billed to_____

2

An example of how one collecting area leads to another. An Adams Express Co. C.O.D. envelope pre-printed from Colt's Pat. Firearms Co. Note inquiry is on .45 caliber U.S. Army Pistol. Circa — 1885.

These package scales made by Howe Scale Co. for Wells Fargo around 1914 are red and have the original gold leaf markings still on them. These marked scales are very desirable today, as most were never marked.

The Railway Express Agency Air Express porcelain sign o multicolored enamel dates from the first use of airplanes fo carrying express packages. Circa — 1930.

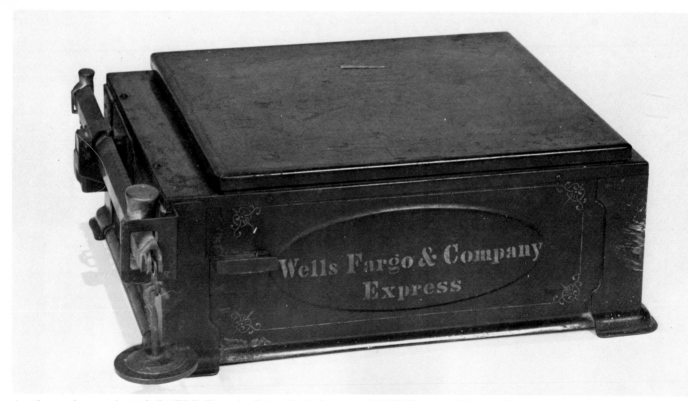

Another package scale made for Wells Fargo by Triner Scale Co. around 1917. These are black and have gold lettering. These scales, althoug later, are rarer than the Howe scales. This set was used in the Wells Fargo office in Holbrook, Arizona.

1

Of extreme rarity are original express co. special agent's badges. Before 1918 most express co's had few special agents. (Note that they were also called special officers.) The Railway Express Agency badge on right was used by deputies of the special agents.

# ADVERTISING

*Jim Cope*

Beautiful advertising has been produced by the gun and ammunition companies continually since the late 1800's.

Collectors, however, consider the advertising from the late 1800's through the 1920's to be the most beautiful, and therefore the most collectable.

The most popular of all gun advertising is the cartridge board. Winchester produced six different boards. These were issued in 1874, 1879, 1884, 1886, 1890 and 1897. The 1890 board is known as the "Single W", while the 1897 issue is known as the "Double W". The 1897 board is the largest of the Winchester boards.

One of the most attractive boards was issued by the Union Metallic Cartridge Company. This is a very large board, mounted under glass, with a heavy wood frame marked U.M.C.

Also popular are the A.B. Frost calendars put out by Winchester in the 1890's. However, beware of recent reprints. They are marked as such in the lower margin, but that is easily trimmed off. The originals have round metal gromets to hold the calendar pad in place, while the reprints have staples. Another way to tell the originals is that the metal strips at top and bottom have a striped design. On the reprints this is solid black.

Other popular items include The Winchester Dogs. These are found in several sizes and the largest, 32 inches by 42 inches, is the most valuable. These beautiful signs originally came in wood frames, sometimes marked Winchester. Those with unmarked frames are not as desirable.

Advertising is well on its way to recognition as a legitimate form of art. None is more beautiful than that which illustrates the Old West and gun and hunting pleasures.

Remington-UMC paper poster 18" x 26".

Winchester 1925 calendar 15½ X 21½.

Remington Arms paper poster 17″ X 25″.

Winchester 1913 tin sign, Spanish edition 30″ X 36″.

Austin Powder Co. 1900 calendar 15″ X 29½″.

Winchester 1911 paper poster 15″ X 30½″.

Harrington & Richardson Arms Co. 1907 calendar 14″ X 27″.

"Infallible" powder paper poster. 20" X 26".

Peters 1919 calendar 14″ X 27″.

Peters 1909 paper poster 14″ X 27″.

Winchester 1907 paper poster 15½″ 29½″.

Union Metallic Cartridge Co. 1902 calendar 13½″ X 26½″.

Peters 1909 calendar 14″ X 27″.

Winchester paper poster 15″ X 28½″.

Hopkins & Allen paper poster 10″ X 26½″.　　　　Winchester 1912 paper poster 16½″ X 30″.

Ithaca Guns paper poster 16½" X 28".

Union Metallic Cartridge Co. paper poster 15½" X 25".

Remington UMC paper poster 17″ X 24″.

Medlar · SPENCER · IOWA

# WESTERN PHOTOGRAPHY

## The Image of the Old West

*Emory A. Cantey, Jr.*

Nothing reflects the true image of the Old West more reliably than photographs taken during that period in our history. True, the equipment was crude, the conditions were harsh and trying, and many of the photographs were staged. Nevertheless, early Western photography is our most accurate and personal record of that era.

Photography is the finest medium ever invented for recording what the people of an era looked like, what they wore, what kind of weapons and tools they used, and the type of buildings they lived and worked in. Every photograph is in its own special way unique and individual. Collections of photographs from the American West are among the most valued first hand documents of this country's historical past.

Keep in mind that all Western photography is indeed rare. Most of this photography was produced in paper mediums (carte-de-visite, studio cabinet cards, etc.) and a lesser amount in tintypes, ambrotypes, and daguerreotypes. While thousands were taken, the survival rate has been quite low. Although photography was taken in the West in daguerrian mediums as early as the 1840's, the most popular types, other than personalities and gold mining, are those of cowboys, scouts, and trappers who came later.

Most cowboy photographs were staged and posed. In the days of the Old West, cowboys had their photographs taken in town after the long, dusty trail drives. They washed off the trail dust and dirt of the past weeks and changed into new clothing. However, if the cowboy could not afford a new outfit, the photographer supplied him with clothing for the photograph. This readily explains the crispness of the clothing in most cowboy photography. Quite obviously, no self-respecting cowboy wanted to send a photograph home to his sweetheart or family showing him dirty and haggard from the trail drives.

By the early 1870's, the law in the West strictly prohibited the wearing of firearms into any of the most famous cowtowns such as Dodge, Tombstone, Hays, etc. Those who believe otherwise have often been misled by the various movie myths. The photographer provided cowboys with handguns, holster rigs, rifles and shotguns for posing. These guns, used as props, vary distinctly from old flintlocks to the most modern cartridge arms of the particular era. In other words, whatever was handy at the moment was used in the photograph. The cowboy wanted a gun somewhere in evidence to complete the impression of a well-equipped man of the range. For the collector, the addition of various types of weapons adds to the value of the photograph.

One of the most prominent aspects of Western cowboy photography is the age of the men in the photographs. Inexperienced people have stated these could not possibly be photographs of real cowboys, because the men portrayed are simply too young. This is a myth. The average age of cowboys in the 1868-1900 period was the mid-twenties. They rarely continued in the trade past their forties due to the tremendous hardships inherent in their profession. In this early period of our country, men came of age at thirteen to fourteen years old. Consequently, the shy teenager stiffly standing in front

Four Texas Rangers of Company D in the late 1880's. They are heavily armed and ready for a scout. Standing, left, is Ranger, Walter Durbin. All four of these men later died violent deaths.

## DAGUERREOTYPES

The earliest form of photography, called a daguerreotype, was invented by Louis Jacques Mande Daguerre in the 1830's. This delicate image was produced by the camera directly onto sheet copper with a silver oxide process. This process caused the actual image to have a distinctive mirror image quality and the image must be viewed by slightly turning it out of the direct light to the right or left. It was popular in the United States in the 1840 to 1850 period and is quite rare in Western photography, making an appearance mostly in the early Gold Rush period in California. Sizes vary greatly and are graded in value. The largest sizes are the most rare and valuable. Authenticated photographs of personalities on Western subjects in this medium should be considered most valuable. They were placed in fancy cases for their protection.

## AMBROTYPES

Ambrotypes were produced by a process similar to daguerreotypes except that they were produced directly on glass and are the most delicate images ever produced. For this reason, they were not popular and most were produced in the 1850-1865 period. Ambrotypes were most common in the Civil War era but a few were taken in the West as late as the early 1870's. Sizes vary greatly and are graded as daguerreotypes, the largest being the most valuable. These images were also placed in fancy cases for their protection. Western images in this medium should be considered extremely valuable, second only to daguerreotypes.

## STUDIO CABINET CARDS

Studio Cabinet cards are the most common photographic medium. Produced in the 1860-1920 period, these paper photographs were mounted on cardboard mounts bearing the photographer's name and address. The actual photograph was developed from a glass negative in a process quite similar to modern photography. There was no real standard of size but the most common size was a 5¾" X 4" photograph mounted on a 6½" X 4¼" mount. Virtually all of the known, famous photographs of Western personalities are in this medium.

## CARTE-DE-VISITES

The Carte-de-visite was essentially a small cabinet card, the size of an early business card (thus carte-de-visite or photo business card). They were first produced as early as the late 1850's and remained popular until the turn of the century. These paper images were produced by the same procedure as cabinet cards, from a glass negative. The cardboard mounts often, but not always, bear the photographer's name and address on the reverse side of the mount. The most common size was a 3¼" X 2¼" photograph on a 4¼" X 2½" mount. Some important personality photographs were produced in this medium but they should be considered rare.

## TINTYPES

Tintypes have no negatives. They are photographic images developed and produced directly on sheets of tin, then cut to size. This process was used from the early 1860's until the early 1900's and was a common medium, following the studio cabinet card in popularity. There were no mounts required and the sizes varied extensively from very small to very large (with larger sizes being most rare). The most common size was 3¾" X 2¾". Authenticated photographs of Western personalities in this medium should be considered quite rare.

A full plate daguerreotype of Brown, Henry & Co.'s store in Sacramento, Calif. Circa 1851. Full plate daguerreotypes are scarce, but identifiable Western ones are extremely scarce. Brown, Henry & Co. was a clothing firm which was totally destroyed in the great fire of 1852. They never went back into business.

f the camera was in most cases a tough and competent rail hand' back on the range.

Cowboy images have frequently been misunderstood. Posed but unstaged photographs are rarer than posed and staged views. Certain candid outdoor views are the rarest types. However, this aspect does not readily affect the value of any individual photograph. Most of the favorite collectable photographs are the posed and staged studio cabinet cards and tintypes.

These photographs are a valuable source of information about the dress, arms, leather, general ages, and life styles of the American cowboy. In this regard, it does not matter to the experienced collector whether the photograph is staged or not. The photographs are staged with the equipment, arms and clothing of the particular era, and the historical significance of these valuable insights is the most important value judgement.

Images of this type were taken literally all over the West. Photographers' marks impressed on the cardboard mounting of the carte-de-visites and studio cabinet cards cover most of the Western states. With some diligence, one may hope to accumulate quite a composite collection of cowboy images in these mediums. Some of these were taken by such notables as Curtis, Huffman, Kirkland, Burge, Fly, and Chamberlain. Others were taken by itinerant photographers with nothing but a sheet for a backdrop.

Similar views can be obtained concerning the early Western scouts, trappers, and frontiersmen of the era. The most popular example of this type show men dressed in buckskin clothing. These images may be unidentified mountainmen, trappers, scouts, or just men on a lark. They can even be cowboys who happen to prefer the fancier buckskin outfits more than the usual clothing of their trade. However, one also finds such famous figures as Kit Carson, Captain Jack Crawford, Texas Jack Omohundro, Bill Cody, Wild Bill Hickok, and others.

This type of photography has real eye appeal. Historically, such pictures furnish us with excellent examples of the type of buckskin outfit worn during a particular period. These images can be found in various photographic mediums from the 1840's to the 1900's. However, they should be considered extremely rare in daguerrain photography.

There are all kinds of buckskin dress. There is the simplified clothing of the early trapper with very little frills. There is the fancier buckskin outfit of the military scouts and the mountainmen with long fringe and Indian beadwork. Finally there are the super fancy buckskin outfits of the great showmen such as Buffalo Bill Cody and Captain Jack Crawford. These outfits were designed for the absolute ultimate in showmanship and not for any practical value. Some of these types show men in elaborate, long fringe, ornamented American Indian beadwork wearing fur collars and cuffs and exotic animal skins. How people must have stared when someone such as Bill Cody rode into the ring in one of these fantastic outfits!

More than just the outfits themselves, these photographs usually have other attractions for the collector. One encounters such things as beautiful, silver mounted flintlocks and percussion rifles, fancy stocked and engraved Winchesters, ivory and pearl gripped Colts of all models, fancy holster rigs, and the fanciest of headgear. A few early views even show examples of the traps used by early trappers as well as many other tools of his trade. More spectacular than any of these, perhaps, are the views showing the buckskinners with live animals. One daguerreotype of note shows a heavily bearded old mountainman with his pet bird sitting on his shoulder! Others exhibit show men with such famous American Indians as Sitting Bull and Geronimo.

Views can run the entire spectrum of price ranges. Their prices depend on such factors as personalities,

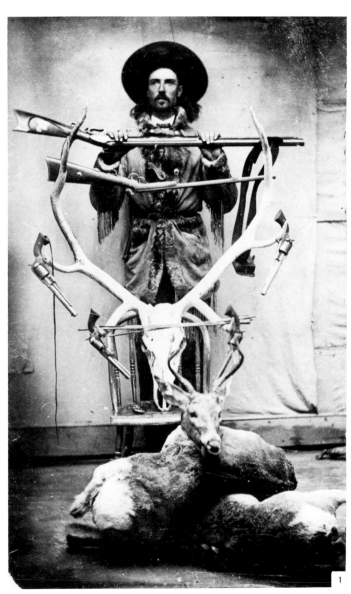

A first rate photograph of an early buckskin dressed hunter of the 1870's. He has a complete fortress of arms of several types as well as recent kills. Notice the makeshift sheet backdrop of the itinerant photographer.

pecial effects within the photographs, photographic mediums, etc. Their price ranges, therefore, can begin as low as fifteen dollars each and as high as the low thousands. In this area of Western photography collecting, the value is based almost solely on how much the highest bidder will pay for the privilege of owning a particular photograph.

Though personalities, cowboys, and buckskinners, are the most popular subjects in the field of photography collecting, they are certainly not the only types that are collectable and desirable. One must not forget such areas as the American Indian and the highly desirable daguerrian images of California gold mining.

Photographic views of American Indians are highly desirable. Many collectors specialize in these views alone. They can be found in daguerreotypes taken from the late 1830's through the mid 1850's, in ambrotypes taken in the 1850's and 1860's, and in tintypes taken between the 1860's and the early 1900's. Carte-de-visites were commonly taken in the late 1860's or early 1870's, and studio cabinet cards were taken from the 1860's to the early 1900's.

Generally speaking, the finest examples are in the earliest mediums, namely daguerreotype, ambrotype, tintype, and carte-de-visite. However, the later cabinet cards are of such a spectacular nature that they are extremely attractive to collectors. Once fairly common, these exceptional views have become quite rare due to the supply and demand factor. Consequently, they have risen in value quite dramatically over the last few years.

The most valuable views are the early daguerrian photographs of the Californian gold mining era. These views are usually outdoor scenes showing the various mining operations and the miners at work. They generally date in the 1840's and early to mid 1850's.

Various types and eras of photography are collected for photographic medium, content, age, condition, photographer's marks and artistic quality. American Western photography is the epitomy of photography collecting because of its specific content and historical value. Collectors in this field are often just as pleased with a paper photograph of excellent quality and content as they are with a daguerreotype of similar quality and content. Consequently, as paper photographs are somewhat more abundant than daguerreotypes and ambrotypes, this category of collecting affords the collector a wider range of possibilities. For this reason, it is an excellent collecting field for anyone.

The five areas above, however, do not take into consideration numerous other areas that are considered collectable. These include scenes of early Western towns, trail drives, chuckwagons, wagon trains, stage coaches and ranches. Occupationals, such as lawmen wearing their star or shield badges, are highly collectable.

Historically, one automatically thinks of photographs of known personalities when considering Western photography. Of course, these particular images are among the rarest and most prized of any collection of this type.

Virtually every collector of Western photography searches for these literally priceless photos.

It is a serious mistake for an amateur to attempt to authenticate a photograph thought to picture a famous personality. The process of comparing any photograph to that of another previously authenticated one is, at best, tricky and many trained professionals make mistakes. It is worthwhile to remember that collectors tend to see what they want to see, and are not always as objective as they should be.

Exceptional early tintype photograph of a young buckskinner. The photograph is very artistically posed as well as historically interesting. He wears a fringed buckskin shirt, has a single shot rifle in his lap, a pipe in his mouth and looks ready to go buffalo hunting.

On the far left of this building in this photograph is one of the banks that the famous James, Younger gang tried to rob in Northfield, Minn. in 1876. Here, the gang met its Waterloo. This photograph is in many respects rarer than photographs of the gang itself.

This is a truly beautiful outdoor view, a cabinet, of a cowboy and his horse. It was probably taken in Arizona or New Mexico. Take note of the unusual brands and markings on the rump of the horse.

An exceptional outdoor view of an early Western general store.

1

Famous photograph of Virgil W. Earp. Bat Masterson dated the photograph as 1885. However, he was mistaken. This original is from the album of his wife, Alvira. She dated it 1882 on the back of the photograph. It was probably taken in Tombstone shortly before he was shot down and nearly killed.

A striking view of an unarmed peasant shot by the Federales.

Winchester carbines, holster rigs, and an extremely rare pair of animal skin chaps grace this fine cabinet view of two cowboy frontiersmen of the 1870's. It was probably taken in Texas or New Mexico as the photographer has a Spanish name.

Cabinet view of the famous Western pioneer, Big Foot Wallace Texas. Wallace was an early Texan, frontiersman, Indian fighter, ar Frontier Texas Ranger. He served under Captain Hays. He holds h Sharps Buffalo rifle in his lap.

A closeup from a group outdoor view of Company D, Texas Rangers in 1889. Captain Frank Jones is the man on the extreme right pointing his pistol.

n-death cabinet view of the famous Dalton gang after being shot down during their ill fated attempted robbery of two banks at one time in offeeville, Kansas in the 1890's. The two men in the middle are Daltons. The two others on each end are gang members. Notice the little boy king a peep at the famous outlaws through the wall.

SARONY. 68c BROADWAY.

BUFFALO BILL

Early carte-de-visite photograph of Buffalo Bill Cody taken in the early 1870's by the famous photographer, Napoleon Sarony. Buffalo Bill was a scout at this time and an occasional stage actor. He did not start his own Wild West show until the 1880's.

This is a rare carte-de-visite photograph of the famous scout, K Carson. This photograph is probably an early copy of an earlier ph tograph taken in the late 1850's or early 1860's. However, any orig nal photograph of Carson is a real prize.

George Armstrong Custer, leader of the U.S. Cavalry forces at the Battle of the Little Big Horn. Below, a very rare mourning card probably given out at his interment at West Point.

An early carte-de-visite of an Indian. This view is posed but not staged.

Indian prisoner between two early frontiersmen. Both frontiersmen are heavily armed with pistols and long arms. This photograph depicts an extremely rare subject matter, especially in an early tintype. It is completely identified on the reverse side.

THE GREAT·NORTH·WEST.

S. J. MURROW, Yankton, Dakota.

46 1st + 2nd Chiefs of the Gros Ventres—

A stereo photograph of Western Indians in full regalia. Stereo cards were viewed through a hand held device and were very popular in the East as Easterners enjoyed seeing what the Wild West looked like from the comfort of their easy chairs.

Clements

1617 Champa St.
Denver, Colo.

# RUSTY RELICS

## Guns That Didn't Survive

*John A. Kopec*

The study and collecting of rusty relic firearms or "dug ups" as some collectors choose to call them, has become one of the newest facets in the Western collectibles field. This is an area of collecting, like so many branches of the antique collecting field, where nostalgia plays an important part. Owners of rusty relics are continually reiterating the phrase, "If only this relic could talk", and this phrase seems to be the catalytic ingredient which plays such an important part in the enjoyment of owning "just one more rusty relic".

When we speak of the survival rate of certain firearms, we find that depending on their original use and era of production that this survival rate can be as low as 3% or possibly around the 10% figure. This in turn means that 90% to 97% of a given gun model was lost or destroyed many years ago. What happened to these guns? Why is their survival rate so low today? Do they still exist someplace?

Our study in this section deals with those guns which didn't survive, but were later found in some remote area, either by chance or by systematic searching.

There is no limit to the kinds of old guns that have been found, Old flintlocks, percussions, Colt Dragoons and even Colt Walker revolvers have been found in the remote regions of the West.

Interest has intensified in the collecting of these old relics because unlike the "mint" firearm, these old relics were actually lost by their owners while being used in the field. Many are found fully loaded, or with only one or two empty fired chambers, while the remaining chambers are still loaded! Some of these revolvers may have been lost during an Indian battle or a stagecoach hold-up. In any event, the percentages are good for rusty relic firearms to continue to be found in years to come.

Rusty relic firearms have been found in ghost town dumps, old out-house sites, caves, under old buildings, or simply lying in the desert or in forest terrain. Since the advent of the metal detector, many have been dug-up in the remote mining camps of the old West. Battlefields, too, will yield military type weapons. Many of these however, have deteriorated to a point where only portions remain. The finest relics are found in the drier areas of the West where they have not been completely disintegrated by excessive moisture.

This Colt Single Action Army, was found near Mexico City in 1974. It had been buried in the late 1800's during the revolution. At that time private citizens were not allowed to own guns. This relic shows traces of its original nickel plating and still has the original ivory grips.

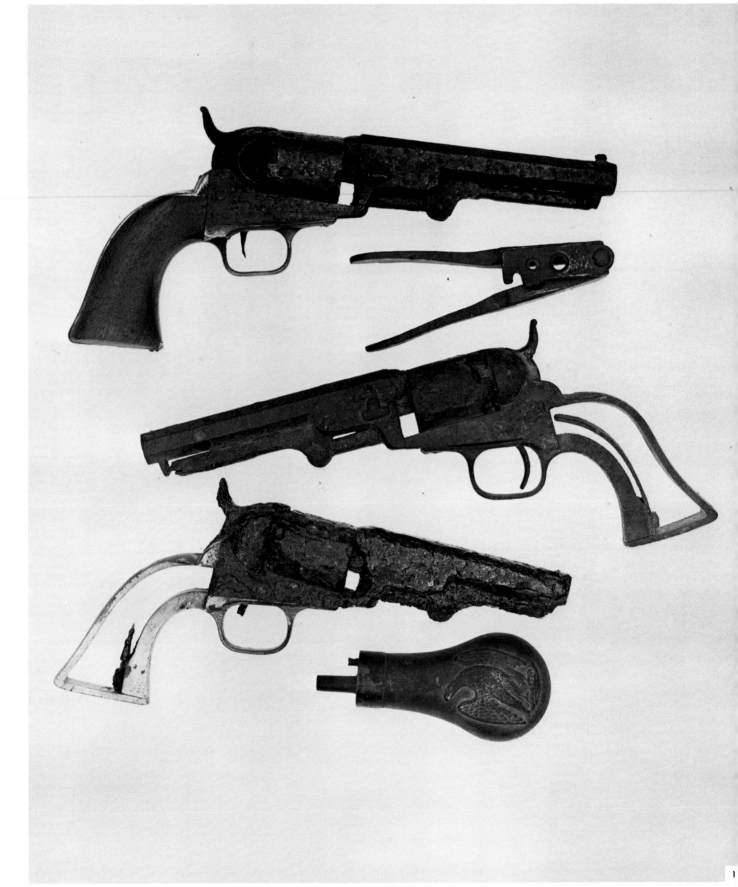

A group of Colt M1849 Pocket revolvers in various stages of deterioration. Top: Serial #26,639 (mfg. 1853) is fairly well preserved and has three chambers loaded. Center: This M1849 Pocket sports a bent grip strap and is serial numbered 168,464 (mfg. 1860), while the lower example is encrusted with heavy rust. Its serial number 241,929 (mfg. 1863) is plainly visible on its silver plated grip straps. An old relic Colt powder flask and a Manhattan bullet mold add interest to this group of revolvers.

## Determining Desirability

What makes one rusty relic firearm more collectable or desirable than another? Collecting rusties is much like gun collecting in general. Those desirable types of collector firearms in the arms collecting field, are usually the same types which are found to be desirable in the rusty relic field. Colts and Winchesters, of course, lead the way. Single Action Colts are among the most sought after types along with the percussion Colts. Guns which have a portion of their original stocks remaining are more desirable than those in a further state of decomposition whose stocks have completely deteriorated. Loaded firearms are more collectable than those which are found unloaded. Those found with spent old copper cartridges in their chambers are interesting and collectable. These bear evidence of being lost while actually being used in the field.

Many stories have come to us regarding the location of rusty relic revolvers or other firearms in the field. One M1849 Colt pocket revolver was found in Bodie before it was made a California State Park. A London Dragoon was found near a tree in a Washington state forest. The illustrated 7½″ Colt Single Action was found beside the All American Canal near El Centro, California. The broken Remington New Model Army revolver came out of Virginia City, Nevada. Relics can be found most anywhere, and do show up in strange places. Lately the exploration of long abandoned privies has proved fruitful in finding relic firearms as well as a host of other antiques and coins.

## Restoration

Should an attempt be made to restore a rusty relic when found? The answer to this question is an emphatic NO! Too many unsuspecting and untrained persons immediately proceed to try to restore a relic firearm when found. We have seen cases where relics were sand blasted, filed, soaked in oil and wire brushed, all attempts to restore something which in reality is unrestorable. The best possible advice we can give is to leave the relic exactly as it was found. Do not attempt to scrape or remove the rust, or to free frozen parts. Any value in a rusty relic would be completely destroyed by these attempts. Relic collectors want their examples to remain exactly in the condition in which they were found. This, of course, adds appeal and a certain nostalgia which could forever be lost by any attempts at restoration.

## Rusty Relic Revolvers

Rusty relic revolvers when found are living proof of their use on a particular battlefield or frontier setting. Of course, it would add interest if the exact location where a given piece was located was noted on a tag affixed to the weapon. In most cases this sort of documentation was never recorded and has long since become obscure. In cases where a particular piece is being presented for sale with a long story that it was found on the Custer Battlefield, our humble advice would be: "Don't

Two Colt Double Action revolvers are shown in this photograph. The upper revolver, an M1878 Double Action sports its original 7½″ barrel, while its trigger is gone. Its cylinder pin was in the process of disengagement when this revolver became lost. The lower example is that of a M1877 Colt Lightning revolver sporting the rarest of all grip types for this model, the one piece hard rubber variant. These grips were discontinued by Colt only a few weeks after production began in 1877. Though heavily encrusted with rust, its silhouette is easily discernable.

Colt's M1860 Army revolver was the principle Union Army hand gun of the Civil War period. This group of three M1860 Army revolvers shows them in three stages of deterioration. Top: A Military cut for stock model, still has its original grips, but is missing the loading lever unit as are the others. The center illustration, a civilian model, not cut for stock, #139,344, was manufactured in 1863. The lower revolver also a military version shows signs of advance deterioration as well as some abuse.

1

Two percussion era relic revolvers and one partial revolver are shown in this group. The top revolver is a Colt 1851 iron strapped Navy, a very desirable variant. The center example is a Remington New Model Navy revolver, Caliber 36, with three of its chambers loaded and capped. The lower example is the rear portion of a Remington new model Army revolver, hammer cocked, which may have been run over by a wagon, resulting in its severely damaged condition. It was found in Virginia City, Nevada.

2

believe a word of it". If you buy a particular relic, buy it only on its own merits, and not on the merits of a long story which may be attached to it. Remember, old revolvers are especially desirable if they have their original grips and are either partially or fully loaded. Engraved or inscribed pieces are also particularly desirable. These are the characteristics which add "flavor" to the piece, not an undocumented story which may go along with it. Large frame revolvers like the Colt Dragoons, Army or Navy models and Single Actions seem to have more appeal than do the smaller "pocket-size" revolvers. These smaller pocket revolvers are interesting if found loaded, and those with brass frames appeal to collectors if the brass has not been polished! Remember it took nature possibly a hundred years to patina that brass the color it is now and a moment of careless polishing can destroy a hundred years of natural patina finish.

# Relic Rifles

Rifles were an integral part of the old West, both from the military aspect and the civilian standpoint. So we find relics of both categories have been lost in various locations throughout the West. They are there. It's up to you to find one. Relic rifles come in several styles and categories. Among the most desirable are the brass framed Henrys and M1866 Winchesters. These may be found "tacked", indicating prior Indian ownership. Old military Springfields are quite desirable, especially if found with a portion or all of their wooden stocks intact. Relic Indian War Springfield Carbines and rifles have particular appeal to the Indian War or "Custer buff". After all, there can be little doubt of the historical significance of such a piece.

Like the Colt Single Action, the Winchester M1873 rifle and carbine are well represented in the relic collecting field. After all there were thousands produced, they were used extensively, and ultimately many were lost. Fortunately for the relic collector, one of the most colorful and desirable rifles, "The Gun That Won The West", is also one of the most abundant types found in relic condition today.

Many relic rifles are found showing evidence of severe abuse. These were used as hammers and pry-bars before being discarded by their former owners. Some show evidence of a jammed chamber from which a spent cartridge could not be extracted. Examples such as these tend to tell a story of their early demise, and indicate that they had been discarded by their owners rather than unintentionally lost.

Turning now to rifle relics, we show a group of interesting Winchesters: The upper rifle is a brass framed M1866, showing Indian tacking which was dug up by a potato farmer in Arizona. The center rifle is a M1873 which was found at Salt River, Arizona; while the lower relic is a Model 1886 Winchester.

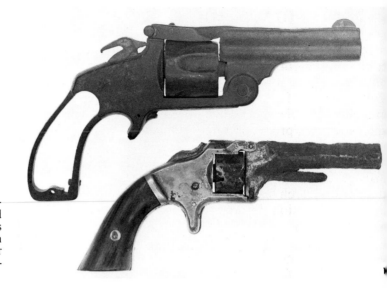

Two relic Smith & Wesson revolvers are shown in this illustration. The upper revolver a .38 Single Action was evidently used as a hammer before being discarded. The lower revolver is their Model 1, second issue in 22 R.F. caliber, showing much of its original silver plate, over a brass frame. Its serial number (57,622) is clearly visible on the butt strap and indicates manufacture sometime between 1860 and 1868.

A first model Springfield M1873 Carbine relic. This was, of course, the principle weapon of the U.S. cavalry during the Indian Wars period. Though this carbine (#39,311) has no significant traceable ancestry, its serial number falls between two recognized Custer period carbines, #39,253, a 7th Cavalry re-captured example and #39,448 an example captured from a Cheyenne. (Ref.: Custer Battle Guns by John S. de Monte...

This illustration is of three interesting rifle relics. The upper relic is a M1873 Springfield Fencing rifle ever made to fire ammunition, it was use in bayonet training exercises. The center relic is a frame and barrel from a Winchester "Hi-Wall" rifle found in California's Mother Lode. The lower rifle is a Marlin-Ballard which was found near Laramie, Wyoming.

# Historical Information

In those instances where the serial number of a relic condition firearm is still readable, some historical information may be obtained. In the case of percussion Colts, most are found with brass guards and their serial numbers are clearly visible. These can be checked against known production figures and at least the year of manufacture can be determined. Colt Single Actions, if found with readable serial numbers can be researched through the Colt factory by sending the historian the standard research fee of $15.00. Precise shipping and ultimate destination information may be obtained in many instances.

Brass-framed relic Winchesters can also be researched through the Buffalo Bill Museum in Cody, Wyoming by sending them the standard $15.00 fee and requesting historical information on that particular Winchester. Other pertinent information can be gathered on many relic pieces by researching gun books devoted to a particular model.

As time progresses we believe we will see Rusty Relic collecting begin to emerge and become an accepted facet of the arms collecting field. We believe that full fledged displays will soon appear at the better gun shows throughout the country, and that this field will become recognized as an accepted part of the arms collecting fraternity. Such displays have the potential of becoming especially interesting if related relics of bygone days are displayed along with the firearms. Such relics as spent cartridge cases, powder flasks, and loading accessories would add to making such a display a "winner".

# Faking

As we begin to see the price of the true relics climb, we note that a new rash of "fakers" is emerging. These unscrupulous individuals who never miss an opportunity to make a buck, are taking the old "suicide special" revolvers which have very little collector interest, soaking them in muriatic acid and letting them rust a while. These are now showing up at gun shows in an effort to be passed off as rusty relics. Several "Italian Walkers" have also been noted which have been through this process. Some are difficult to detect, others are clearly detectable. Always remember, new rust is red in color, while old rust will turn a dark brown. If you see a relic sporting a red rust color, you can be assured it has been recently "helped" in the aging process.

Though the Rusty Relic field is quite vast, we would like to present a few of the various available types which are found in collections today. Their values are climbing, along with an intense interest in this relatively new field of collecting. We hope that you will enjoy the material presented. Nostalgia is what it's all about!

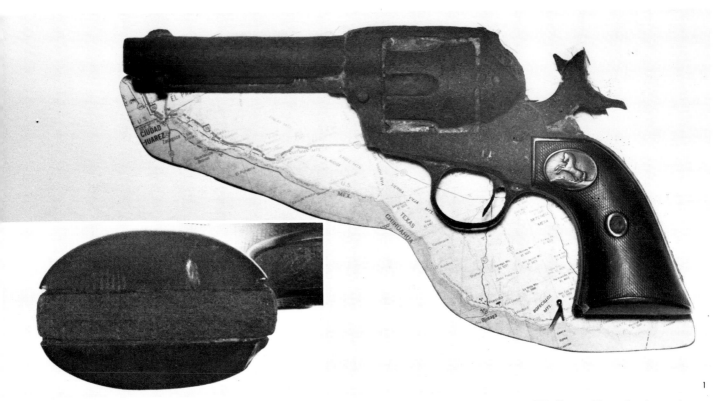

This Colt Single Action Army was found in 1975 in a dry gulch near the Rio Grande, near the mining town of Terlingua. From the six notches on the butt of the grip, the position of the hammer, and the fired and unfired cartridges, it would appear that this gun was lost during a shoot out.

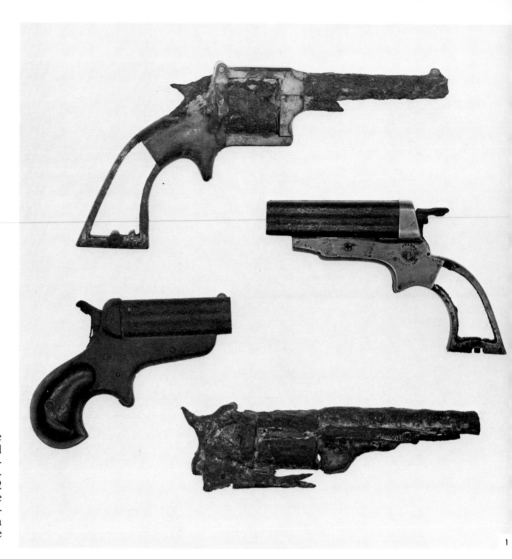

A group of four pocket pistols: The upper example is a Lucius W. Pond pocket revolver which was manufactured circa 1861 to 1870. The left illustration is that of a Sharps & Hankins 32 Caliber pepperbox, while on the right we see a Sharps brass frame 32 caliber Pepperbox. The lower example is a relic of a Colt Pocket Navy conversion in a state of extreme deterioration.

The smaller pocket type revolvers in relic condition, when found, can add interest to a collection. The upper revolver is Colts brass framed "House Pistol" (mfg. 1870's) in caliber 41 R.F. The lower example is a Whitney 22 caliber revolver, loaded with copper cased cartridges. It too sports a brass frame, but this particular frame was gold plated!

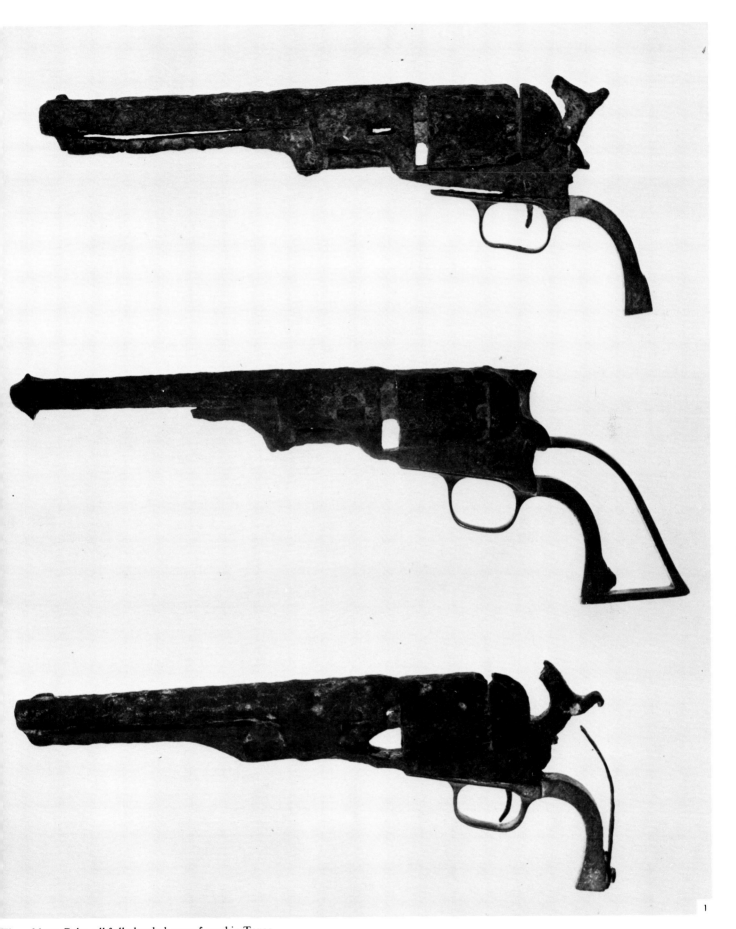

These Navy Colts, all fully loaded, were found in Texas.

# THE BADGE

## Symbol of Law and Order

*John Bates*

The historical significance of the law badge spans a period of time from approximately 1840 to the present and has been an integral part of American history. The badge has represented authority, hope, power and at times corruption. As the bandana and musk have effectively identified the outlaw, so the badge has been the symbol of law and order. Many well-known Americans have been closely associated and identified with law badges including: the Earp brothers, Ben Thompson, Pat Garrett, Heck Thomas, and in more current times Elliot Ness and Buford Pusser. The list is long and impressive.

Law badges, in particular those worn openly on the chest area of civilian clothing or uniform to distinguish them from those worn primarily on hats, are truly an American phenomenon. Many historians theorize that the American law badge can trace its roots to the crests and coats of arms generally worn suspended around the neck as used in early colonial America to identify military officers and later, night watchmen. The primary difference between the American system of identifying and defining the authority of the law officer from most other areas of the world is that the focus in America has been on the breast badge while in other areas it was and still remains the uniform. Where uniforms are the symbol of law and police authority, badges are usually nothing more than insignia attached to collars or shoulder to designate rank, unit or organization. Historically, in the United States the badge, in many cases despite the type of clothing to which it was pinned, is the symbol of authority. Because of this difference and many other factors, the American law badge represents a fertile field for collecting.

## Age

Since we are dealing with such a long period of use it is possible to select a period of time to suit the individual collector. Generally speaking, there are no absolute or fool-proof methods of pinpointing the exact age of a badge. Exceptions exist of course in those badges which are inscribed or dated as part of the badge, but these are the exceptions rather than the rule. The vast majority of badges must be dated using other means. The methods of dating a badge, at least to an approximate age, involve various techniques.

Unfortunately the vast majority of American law badges were never marked by the manufacturer. However, those that are can be dated rather easily by checking city directories. Names and addresses of manufacturers on badges are most often referred to as "Hallmarks."

Badge design or shape is one of the least reliable methods to use for dating badges simply because almost all designs shown in antique badge manufacturing catalogs are available in currently manufactured badges. The one exception I have found in researching newer catalogs is the octagonal shaped badge which doesn't seem to be currently available.

Law badges have been manufactured from a wide variety of materials. The two most popular materials used have been brass and nickel silver. Early post Civil War era badges were most often made of plain unplated brass, while later brass badges were plated. Badges from about 1890-1930 were most often nickel plated. Gold plated nineteenth century badges were usually intended for issue to ranking officers. Solid nickel was a very popular and durable badge material in use from at least the early 1880's until approximately 1940. Solid silver and gold badges apparently have been in use from at least the 1860 period and are available today on special order. The 1912 C.G. Braxmar Co. catalog lists the following finishes or materials available; gold, rolled gold, gold plate, silver and nickel.

By far the most frequently used method of dating badges is by the type of pin and catch used on the reverse. The pin and catch are frequently called "jeweler's findings." Caution should be exercised since "jeweler's findings" are not absolute as to date of use. As a rule of thumb, barring evidence that the pin or catch has been replaced, findings can be used to date within general age ranges. An early type of "finding" called the "t-pin" or European pin with a "shell" catch is shown in photo no. 1. This pin and catch were seldom used after 190. The exception is the jeweler-made solid gold or silver badge where this type of pin can be found in use today. Photo no. 2 shows a sheet metal joint with pin and "tube" catch both of which were used until approximately 1900. Photo no. 3 is an early private detective badge with a one-piece spring pin and catch. This type of finding was a popular and extensively used pin from at least the late nineteenth century until 1940. Photo no. 4 demonstrates a similar pin with the exception of a "cover" plate on the pin. The plate, although not always used, tends to date the badge later than those without the cover. Photo no. 5 showing a hallmarked badge with a large tube catch is an early Galveston, Texas badge circa 1870-80.

An unusual catch called the "fork" or "thumbnail" can be found in use from as early as the 1850's-1940's. was not as desirable a catch as many and frequently was replaced with later type catches. A later catch frequently encountered is the "bullet", circa 1930-present. One-piece patented catches and pins of two styles are often found on less expensive badges. Both usually bear patent numbers 2,066,969 (Farnham's patent circa 1937) and 2,383,012 (Morehouse patent circa 1945). Both are still in current use.

Other techniques which might help the badge collector approximate the date of badges are the study of old photography showing lawmen wearing badges, and old badge catalogs.

The gun that killed "Billy the Kid", Colt Single Action serial no. 55093 and a solid gold badge presented to Pat Garrett by A. J. Fountain in 188

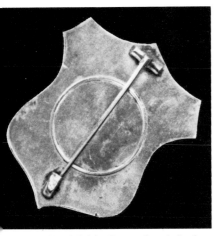

re 1900 Philadelphia, Pennsylvania badge, rass with nickel plate with a good example f an early "t-pin" and a "shell" catch.

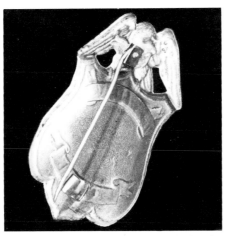

Reverse of early Dallas, Texas badge in solid nickel, showing sheet metal joint and "tube" catch.

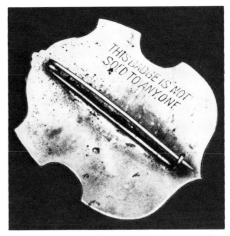

Reverse of early Private Detective badge showing simple one piece pin and catch without cover plate.

ix-point nickel star showing one-piece pin ncorporating cover plate, circa 1920.

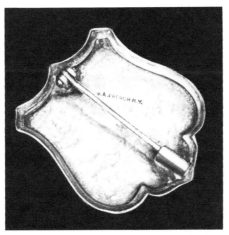

Reverse of early Galveston, Texas badge, showing hallmark and "tube" catch, circa 1870-90.

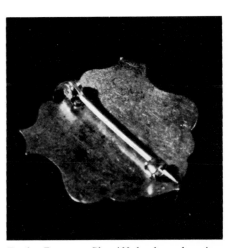

Early Deputy Sheriff badge showing "tongue" catch, circa 1910.

# DEPUTY

# U. S. MARSHAL

Early ribbon designed to be worn as hat band, circa 1880.

A good example of a "stock" badge with a very collectable title. Decoration on points and center are hand-stamped.

Circa 1890, nickel silver, Dallas badge; center star is separately applied. Lettering is filled with the commonly encountered soft black paint.

A good example of an early, plain, shield badge with line cuts (engraving) above and below letters. This, plus small stamped decoration, is characteristic of early badges.

Early Butte, Montana badge with "tick" engraving and center star which was soldered into the shield, circa 1900. Nickel plate over brass.

An outstanding example of a highly desirable style of badge. Tip-offs to the early nature of this badge are its title which includes the use of "City", and the extensive use of hand engraving.

A beautiful solid gold badge presented to Tarrant County, Texas Deputy Sheriff circa 1890.

A desirable shape, title and location make this Western badge a sought after item. This badge is nickel silver with stamped decoration and a one-piece pin and catch, circa 1900-20.

This exceptional seven-point star is sterling silver and hand engraved. The lettering is filled with hard fired black enamel. Circa 1900-1925.

A good example of a "stock" badge. It is nickel plated over brass and has the early characteristics of border engraving and line cuts over and under the title, circa 1900.

# Shape, Design and Size

The most commonly encountered shapes in American law badges are the star and the eagle top shield. However, there are many variations even in these basic shapes. It is difficult to use shapes as direct indications of age since most shapes have been repeated frequently over the last 140 years. Shape and design do, however, represent one of the more interesting areas of variety in badge collecting. Popular belief supported by Hollywood films suggests that certain shapes were linked directly to specific geographic areas. Although there is evidence that particular shapes were more popular in some locales than others, it is safe to say that all shapes were used throughout the country. Generally, badges come in four sizes:

1. **Miniatures:** Usually less than 1 inch by 1 inch and primarily used for wearing in lapels of civilian clothing.
2. **Small:** Approximately 1½ inches and generally considered a "wallet" or off duty type badge.
3. **Medium:** Approximately 2-2½ inches by 2-2½ inches, a working badge in many jurisdictions.
4. **Large:** Approximately 3-3¼ inches by 3-3¼ inches, considered a standard uniform badge in many departments.

The basic shapes and designs observed by the author are:

1. **Star:** A very popular and early shape used throughout the country, and especially in the West.
   A. Seven-point star: Particularly popular in California.
   B. Six-point star: The most common type of star encountered.
   C. Five-point star: Less frequently used star shape.
   D. Eight-point star: Rarely used early shape.
2. **Shield:** Along with the star one of the earliest shapes in badges. Despite popular folklore, the shield was highly popular in the early West. Many early Texas badges were shields rather than stars.
   A. Eagle top shield: Early badge catalogs suggest that at least during the 1880's eagle top badges were intended for issue to the larger police departments. In other areas the choice of an eagle top badge seems to have simply been a personal one.
   B. Plain shield: Early shields tend to be rather basic in shape while later shields became highly ornate.
   C. Shield with cut out star: A badge style many times associated with the Western states although not exclusive to this area. Collectors of pre-1920 badges rank this shape as highly desirable.

3. **Round:** Most frequently observed in nineteenth and early twentieth century badges. Infrequently used at present.
   A. Solid round: Usually an early badge used extensively in the North East section of the country circa 1860-1910.
   B. Circle with cut out star center: One of the most popular shapes with collectors, used frequently in the West and also by the federal government.
4. **Oval:** A shape of limited use and then usually pre-1920. Used most often in the New England and Eastern areas.
5. **Octagonal:** Another badge used extensively on the East Coast, usually pre-1920's. The earliest badge of this design I have observed was circa 1860.
6. **Crescent star:** Considered a rare and desirable badge shape with limited use. Examples of this shape are found in both the South and West.
   A solid gold badge of this shape from El Paso, Texas, is known to have been used in 1882. The New Orleans Police Department still uses this design.
7. **Sunburst:** An unusual design, used in Dallas and Houston, Texas, and also in California. The 1912 C.G. Braxmar catalog shows five different examples of this style.
8. **Diamond:** Rarely encountered shape. Few examples of this design are known. This shape is not pictured in any of the current or antique badge catalogs I have observed.

# Titles

Titles appearing on badges are an important consideration for any collector. In fact, titles and locations are by far the primary consideration, with age and material next in order. Badges of various types have been issued for many reasons, some of which have only limited interest to the law badge collector. Even those titles issued to law enforcement personnel are varied, having undergone changes in terms of duties over the years.

As an example, although constables today are in most cases little more than paper servers, in the Old West, constables were front line working law officers. In the same vein, sheriffs were elected officials who many times had little law enforcement experience and rarely ventured beyond administrative duties, leaving the true enforcement duties to their deputies. It should be remembered that a sheriff is a county official, and although they were stationed in a city or town they were not considered sheriff of that city which in all likelihood had its own police force or city marshal. A badge titled "Deputy Sheriff, Kansas City" would not be correct. A title of high interest to early western badge collectors is City Marshal. Smaller towns and cities generally had marshals rather than police forces until they grew to significant size to warrant the larger system. Although, generally an early title, City Marshal is still used today in small towns throughout this country. Badges titled City Police, City Detective or City Constable are generally considered early badges since the designation "city" is rarely seen in the post World War I era. The most frequently encountered antique federal badges are Deputy U.S. Marshal and Special Deputy U.S. Marshal. U.S. Marshal badges are rare. Those marked "Special" were badges issued to special groups, usually law officers of other types such as Texas Rangers or county sheriffs in order to extend their jurisdiction across state or county lines.

Private title badges were fairly common in the early West. Railroads, mining companies, lumber companies, saloons and express companies frequently had their own organized police or guard force. There were also a significant number of early private detective agencies functioning throughout the country in the pre-World War I era. The titles Special Police, Special Agent or Special Officer are frequently found on antique badges from private agencies.

Badges having a title only, such as Police or Deputy Sheriff without reference to location, are "stock" badges. For economic reasons many early small towns or cities simply ordered badges from a catalog without paying for any special added work. Stock badges in 1912 ran as little as $.75 each in nickel, while solid gold was $25.00. Hallmarks on stock badges do not necessarily indicate the area of use, although a stock badge with a western hallmark is more likely to have been used in the West. However, Western towns frequently ordered from large Eastern badge companies.

This Deputy Marshall badge from the Indian Territory is exceptional because of its rare shape, and its title and location. This badge is hand engraved nickel silver.

A nice early Western badge of nickel silver with good patina and wear. Eagle shields were commonly worn in the early West.

A plain "stock" early western badge. This badge was issued by San Antonio, Texas pre-1920. Badge is solid nickel silver with hand engraved border decorations.

One of the finest examples of a handmade early Western badge. In all likelihood this badge was made locally since the reverse shows pattern and construction lines, and the quality is not professional. It is solid nickel silver.

A superb example of a high quality sterling silver hand engraved California badge, with hard fired black enamel lettering. The hallmark reads, "Ed. Jones & Co., Oaklar Cal." and dates from about 1920.

"Named" badges such as this one from Sierra County, California or Sierra County, New Mexico are desirable not only because they are uncommon but also it is possible to research and date use and ownership.

A beautiful federal badge done in sterling silver and red, white and blue enamel. This is a late badge with a Burgess catch.

A beautiful sterling silver with black flush enamel lettering. This California badge dates about 1910.

Many "stock" badges of the period 1890-1920 are highly decorated with both engraving and various forms of stamped design. This nickel silver badge is a good example of this type.

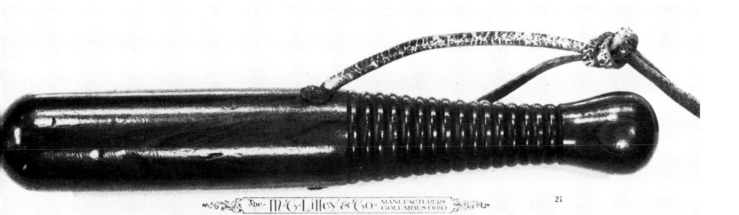

The M G Lilley & Co MANUFACTURERS COLUMBUS OHIO

## STANDARD POLICE EQUIPMENTS

### MACES

Selected from Thoroughly Seasoned Wood. Oil Finish

P-500

Patent Sole Leather Police Club - Swivel Head

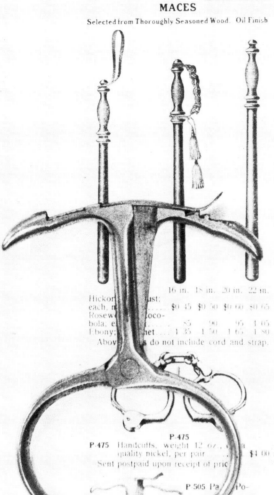

| | | |
|---|---|---|
| 8 inch, weight 9 oz., each | | $1.50 |
| 10 inch, weight 12 oz., each | | 1.75 |
| 12 inch, weight 13 oz., each | | 2.00 |
| 14 inch, weight 16 oz., each | | 2.25 |

Sent express paid when ordered in half-dozen lots.

### BILLET WITH SWIVEL HEAD
### AND STRAP

Made of best high-grade Cocobola wood, with swivel head, so that strap can not be twisted on officer's wrist, each, net............ $1.25

Per dozen, net.................... 13.00

15 inches high and five inches in circum-

16 in. 18 in. 20 in. 22 in.

Hickory, .... just;
each, n ........ $0.45 $0.50 $0.60 $0.65
Rosewo .... oco-
bola, e ........ 85 90 95 1.05
Ebony; .... net 1.35 1.50 1.65 1.80

Above ... s do not include cord and strap.

P-503 Ch ....... r, weight 3
oz ................. $0.75
Handles ....... alike from either side
Sent by .... paid upon receipt of price

**P-475**

P-475 Handcuffs, weight 12 oz., .... quality nickel, per pair ....... $4.00

Sent postpaid upon receipt of pric

P-505 Pa .... Po-
lic .... ppers,
.... ed steel,
nickelplated,
weight 5 oz.,
each......... $1.00

Sent postpaid upon receipt of price.

No P-503
Chain Twister

.... ITH TASSELS

Worsted, full si .... red or blue, each ......... .25
Silk, any col .......
Silk, extra t .... ea

**STRAP**

Rawhide Strap .... ach, .... t

P-505

# POLICE CALLS

ALL PRICES ON THIS PAGE ARE NET—TERMS, CASH WIT[H]

**P-191**

Duplex Call, 3½-inch, with chain, nickel-plated, each, $0 25

...................................$0 35

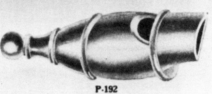

**P-192**

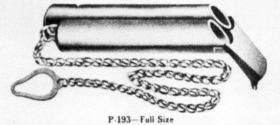

**P-193—Full Size**

......d,.........$0 20     Police Call, Duplex, with bent mouthpiece, chain
                          guard, each.............................$0 25

## [U]NIFORM BUTTONS

### GILT OR NICKEL

| | | |
|---|---|---|
| Coat size | per gross $5 00 | per doz. $0 60 |
| Vest size | per gross 2 50 | per doz. 30 |

We furnish overcoat size in the P style only in gilt or nickel.
Per gross $7 50     per doz. $0 90

We also furnish the P style and Police style buttons in dull
bronze or oxidized color for Khakie and Olive drab uniforms.
Price, coat size, per dozen..............$0 60
Price, vest size, per dozen............. 30

## PATENT SHELL BUTTON COVERS

### FOR CONVERTING PLAIN BUTTONS INTO UNIFORM BUTTONS

Button enclosed on inside

Face of Metal Shell

These [ ] [me]tal in gilt or nickel and fit over plain coat or vest size buttons, [ ]
can change y[ ] [uni]form in a few moments. They are quickly applied and securely fa[ ]
by a slide as [ ] Can be instantly removed.

Co[ ]................................................. $1 20
Ve[st]................................................. 1 00

182

# Building a Collection

The collecting of law badges for most people is a relatively new idea. It is, however, not really a new collecting area, only a little publicized one. For years there was a small but active group of collectors amassing large and important collections without fanfare and among each other.

In the past several years the interest in collecting law badges has grown. Part of this growth has resulted in a tremendous increase in value. Most antique law badges today range in price from about $25.00 to $150.00. Unusual or exceptional badges range from $350.00 to several thousand dollars.

Law badges are generally available at gun shows and in increasing numbers at antique shows, antique stores, and coin and medal shows. Antique law badges are also listed for sale in collectors' periodicals. Now that there are a growing number of collectors, dealers also are emerging. These dealers generally send out periodic lists with badges for sale or trade. Trading among badge collectors is still one of the primary sources for building a collection. Law badge collecting is an extremely broad field and it might be in order to caution new collectors to think about narrowing their area of interest or specialize in certain types, titles or geographic areas. Many collectors including your author tended to accumulate a large number of badges without any direction or theme. Sooner or later as in gun collecting we all tend to have more interest in one area over another. Starting out this way may save having to dispose of many unwanted badges.

Top, a nightstick with built in flask. Middle, is a dress nightstick. Bottom is a presentation nightstick mounted with gold shield and ivory trim.

This exceptionally rare badge was worn by eight federal judges of the Indian courts, starting with Chief Gall and ending with Judge Zahn.

This nice nickel silver badge was made by P.C. Stamping Works, Seattle.

A good example of a frequently encountered "stock" badge used from about 1890 to 1930. Notice the evidence of wear. Pin and catch are of the one piece style without cover plate.

A beautiful sterling badge with the American shield executed in red, white and blue enamel.

A rare five point star made of German silver. The decorative work indicates an early vintage.

A rare badge from the State of Nevada. This nickel silver badge was made by P. and M.K. Company.

This beautiful sterling silver Deputy Sheriff badge from Los Angeles was made by a jeweler and dates about 1900.

"Sheriff" makes this "stock" badge unusual, rather than the more common "Deputy Sheriff" title. Decoration is stamped rather than engraved.

Another nice old nickel silver badge from the State of Nevada.

Atherton IVORY TYPE SALINA, KANS.

Typical early handcuffs used by law enforcement officers in the West.

# Fakes and Reproductions

A growing and serious problem has developed in the past several years in the area of law badge collecting — fakes and reproductions. Although fakes are outright attempts to defraud the buyer and reproductions may start out as "honest" attempts to recreate, the end result is the same. Every badge collector must cautiously approach the purchase of any badge with knowledge and objectivity. With the growing value of badges, the fakers will not only increase their supply, but also their sophistication. Consider the following areas when purchasing antique law badges:

1. **Wear.**

    Most antique badges should show the effects of time and use. These effects show up particularly well under magnification as random marks, lines and dings on the badge surface. Beware of unusually coarse or evenly applied scratches which may indicate attempted artificial aging of the badge. Lettering on badges frequently filled with soft black paint may be found partly missing. Inspection of the bottom of the letter channels should not show any bright scratches indicating intentional removal of the paint. Generally, badge backs show little wear except on outer edges or points which come in contact with clothing. Once again, fakers have attempted to recreate this effect with buffing wheels or steel wool. If the edge wear is uniformly smooth, overly constant or bright be suspicious! Plated badges usually show wear on the high points with plating worn thin or off in those areas.

2. **Patina**

    Patina is the mellowing or softening of color or texture on the surface of a badge created by age or use. Different metals patina differently, with observably different results. Nickel badges patina with a dull, gray appearance over a long period of time which is difficult to reproduce. As a consequence, nickel badges should not be polished. Silver, copper and brass badges patina with a dark blue-black appearance, but unlike nickel this process takes place quite rapidly. Chemical oxidizers are available to create this patina in minutes on silver, copper and brass. Chemically produced patina usually is too evenly applied and rarely shows random differences. Some oxidizers for brass leave a purplish iridescent effect, quite easily spotted. Solid gold, gold plate and gold filled badges show little or no patina.

3. **Pins**

    As indicated earlier, pins and catches represent a fairly accurate method of not only dating badges but also give some indication of authenticity. Check pins and catches to make sure they are not only original to the badge, but also appropriate for the age of the badge. Not all replaced pins represent attempted fakes since hard use many times wore out or broke original pins.

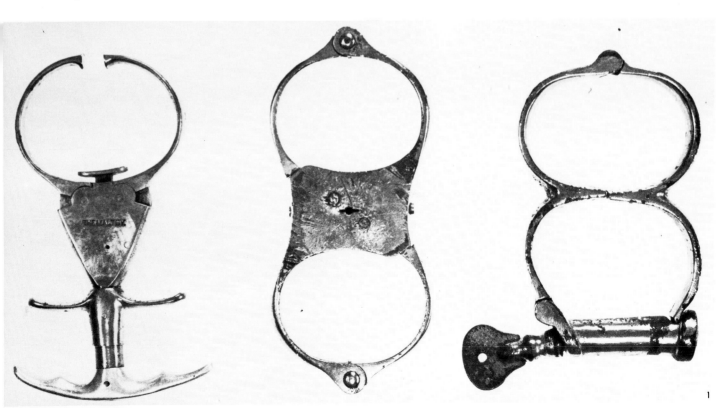

Early and unusual handcuffs and a later model come-along.

Some typical police buckles and a very rare brass padlock, circa 1890.

Conn & Underwood    ALBANY, OR.

# ACKNOWLEDGEMENTS

Many people contributed greatly to this book, and we sincerely appreciate the use of their collections and the information regarding them. Their friendship and support has made publishing this book a real pleasure.

We would especially like to thank the following for sharing their collections and their knowledge:

**Roger Baker,** who has assembled one of the finest collections of saloon advertising in existence.

**John Bates,** co-author of two previous books, "Custom Knives I and II". John has contributed many articles to "Arm Gazette".

**Emory A. Cantey, Jr.,** who has one of the finest private collections of Western photography in the country and has ha many articles published in various magazines.

**Jim Cope,** author of two previous books in the field of advertising, "Soda Water Advertising", and "Collectable Ol Advertising".

**Robert Doyle,** collector and dealer in both gambling artifacts and straight razors. Bob is currently writing a book o the history of straight razors.

**John A. Kopec,** co-author of "A Study of the Colt Single Actions Army Revolver", and a noted authority in the arm collecting field, for his contribution in creating three chapters of this book. John is a Feature Editor for "Arm Gazette".

**Tom Martin,** who has assembled the finest private collection of express memorabilia in the United States.

**Robert O'Dell,** an advanced collector of Western Memorabilia, for his assistance in creating two chapters of this book

**Fauneil Dunn,** who most graciously contributed her beautiful watercolor paintings for illustration both on the cove and in the contents of this book. The eight paintings in the order of their appearance in the book are: "Texas Ranger" "California Spurs", "Mexican Spurs", "Cowboy", "Hoot Gibson", "Wheel of Chance", "Railway Express", an "Sheriff's Office". Copyrights are retained by the artist, Fauneil Dunn.

**Ed Prentiss** and **George T. Jackson, Jr.,** who contributed their collections and most of the fine photography in thi book.

**Bernard R. Levine, Don Beardslee, Jim Cope, Herb Peck, Jr.,** and all of the other fine photographers represented here.

To **Jay Love** and **Jodi Cole,** Taylor Publishing Company, for their cheerful assistance and expert advice.

To my lovely wife, **Sonja,** without whose help and support there would never have been a book.

To all of those collectors who contributed so generously to this book and who are listed in the Picture Credit section.

And finally, to those of you, both collectors and photographers, whom we may have failed to mention, our apologie and our thanks.

# PICTURE CREDITS

## HOLSTERS

Photographed By:

**Ed Prentiss:** Page 8, photo 1 and 2; page 9, photo 2; page 10, photo 1; page 11, photo 1; page 12, photo 1; page 14, photo 1; page 17, photo 1, 2, 3 and 4; page 18, photo 1, 2 and 3; page 19, photo 2; page 20, photo 3; page 21, photo 1 and 2; page 22, photo 1 and 2; page 23, photo 1; page 24, photo 1 and 2; page 26, photo 2 and 3; page 27, photo 1 and 2; page 28, photo 3; page 29, photo 1 and 2; page 30, photo 1, 3 and 4; page 31, photo 1, 2 and 3; page 32, photo 1; page 33, photo 1 and 2; page 34, photo 3; page 35, photo 2 and 4; page 38, photo 2 and 3; page 39, photo 1 and 2; page 41, photo 1, 2 and 3; page 42, photo 2; page 43, photo 2 and 3; page 44, photo 1, 2 and 4; page 45, photo 2, 3 and 4; page 47, photo 1 and 3; page 49, photo 1 and 3; page 50, photo 1 and 3; page 51, photo 2; page 52, photo 3, 4, 5 and 6; page 53, photo 3; page 55, photo 1, 3, 5 and 6; page 56, photo 1 and 2; page 59, photo 1, 2 and 5.

**George T. Jackson, Jr.:** Page 7, photo 1; page 15, photo 1; page 19, photo 3; page 20, photo 1; page 22, photo 4; page 25, photo 1; page 26, photo 1; page 28, photo 1 and 2; page 29, photo 3; page 38, photo 1; page 44, photo 3; page 51, photo 1; page 54, photo 1 and 2; page 56, photo 4; page 58, photo 3.

**Don Beardslee:** Page 18, photo 2; page 19, photo 4; page 31, photo 4; page 35, photo 1 and 3; page 45, photo 1; page 48, photo 1 and 2; page 56, photo 3; page 60, photo 1 and 2; page 61, photo 1.

**Herb Peck, Jr.:** Page 9, photo 1; page 19, photo 1; page 22, photo 3; page 42, photo 1; page 46, photo 1 and 2; page 47, photo 2; page 52, photo 1; page 53, photo 1 and 2; page 58, photo 2.

**Kim Muggleston** (S.L.C. Photographs): Page 34, photo 1 and 2; page 40, photo 1, 2 and 3; page 48, photo 3; page 50, photo 2; page 52, photo 2; page 55, photo 2; page 59, photo 3.

**Robin Jones:** Page 9, photo 3; page 20, photo 2; page 30, photo 2; page 43, photo 1; page 50, photo 4; page 55, photo 4; page 57, photo 1; page 58, photo 1; page 59, photo 4.

From the Collections of:

**Jonathan M. Peck:** Page 17, photo 1, 2 and 3; page 18, photo 1 and 3; page 19, photo 2; page 20, photo 3; page 22, photo 1; page 23, photo 1; page 26, photo 2 and 3; page 31, photo 3; page 38, photo 3; page 39, photo 1; page 44, photo 1; page 45, photo 3 and 4; page 47, photo 1 and 3; page 55, photo 5; page 59, photo 1 and 5.

**George T. Jackson, Jr.:** Page 7, photo 1; page 19, photo 3; page 20, photo 1; page 2, photo 4; page 25, photo 1; page 26, photo 1; page 28, photo 1 and 2; page 29, photo ; page 38, photo 1; page 44, photo 3; page 51, photo 1; page 54, photo 1 and 2; page 5 photo 4; page 58, photo 3.

**John A. Kopec:** Page 8, photo 1 and 2; page 30, photo 3; page 38, photo 2; page 42, pho 2; page 43, photo 2; page 44, photo 2; page 49, photo 2; page 52, photo 4 and 5; page 5 photo 3; page 55, photo 6; page 56, photo 1.

**Bill Mackin:** Page 34, photo 1 and 2; page 40, photo 1, 2 and 3; page 48, photo 3; page 50, photo 2; page 52, photo 2; page 55, photo 2; page 59, photo 3.

**Herb Peck, Jr.:** Page 9, photo 1; page 19, photo 1; page 42, photo 1; page 46, photo 1 an 2; page 47, photo 2; page 52, photo 1; page 53, photo 1 and 2; page 58, photo 2.

**Lew Wight:** Page 9, photo 3; page 20, photo 2; page 22, photo 3; page 30, photo 2; pag 43, photo 1; page 50, photo 4; page 55, photo 4; page 57, photo 1; page 58, photo 1; pag 59, photo 4.

**Phil Spangenberger:** Page 9, photo 2; page 24, photo 1; page 27, photo 2; page 30, phot 1; page 33, photo 2; page 41, photo 2; page 50, photo 3; page 55, photo 1; page 56, phot 2.

**Jack W. Slaughter:** Page 10, photo 1; page 28, photo 3; page 30, photo 4; page 41, phot 1; page 43, photo 2 and 3; page 45, photo 2; page 49, photo 1.

**Bob Eder:** Page 18, photo 2; page 19, photo 4; page 35, photo 1; page 56, photo 3; pag 60, photo 1 and 2.

**Lacy Gaddis:** Page 31, photo 4; page 35, photo 1; page 45, photo 1; page 48, photo 1 an 2; page 61, photo 1.

**Gordon T. Matson:** Page 21, photo 1 and 2; page 31, photo 1; page 41, photo 3; page 5 photo 1; page 52, photo 3.

**Tom Martin:** Page 14, photo 1; page 34, photo 3; page 59, photo 2.

**Jeffrey R. Millet:** Page 32, photo 1; page 35, photo 2 and 4.

**Ed Prentiss:** Page 29, photo 1 and 2; page 44, photo 4.

**Bill Berry:** Page 27, photo 1; page 39, photo 2.

**Emory A. Cantey, Jr.:** Page 2, photo 1; page 15, photo 1.

**Robert Clegg:** Page 22, photo 2; page 31, photo 2.

**John D. Wheeler:** Page 36, photo 2; page 37, photo 1.